HAUNTED CANADA 6

MORE TERRIFYING TRUE STORIES

JOEL A.
SUTHERLAND

Illustrations by
Norman Lanting

Scholastic Canada Ltd.
Toronto New York London Auckland Sydney
Mexico City New Delhi Hong Kong Buenos Aires

Scholastic Canada Ltd.
604 King Street West, Toronto, Ontario M5V 1E1, Canada

Scholastic Inc.
557 Broadway, New York, NY 10012, USA

Scholastic Australia Pty Limited
PO Box 579, Gosford, NSW 2250, Australia

Scholastic New Zealand Limited
Private Bag 94407, Botany, Manukau 2163, New Zealand

Scholastic Children's Books
Euston House, 24 Eversholt Street, London NW1 1DB, UK

www.scholastic.ca

Library and Archives Canada Cataloguing in Publication

Sutherland, Joel A., 1980-, author
Haunted Canada 6 : more terrifying true stories / by Joel A. Sutherland;
illustrated by Norman Lanting.

Issued in print and electronic formats.
ISBN 978-1-4431-4878-8 (paperback).--ISBN 978-1-4431-4879-5 (html)

1. Ghosts--Canada--Juvenile literature. 2. Haunted places--Canada--
Juvenile literature. I. Lanting, Norm, illustrator II. Title. III. Title: Haunted
Canada six.

BF1472.C3S986 2016   j133.10971   C2016-902805-4
                                        C2016-902806-2

Cover credits: hand: Chris Turner/Getty Images;
cover foliage: Matthias Schickhofer/Getty Images).
Interior border: Shutterstock © Filipchuk Oleg.
Illustrations by Norman Lanting.

Thank you to Veronica Kublu of the Department of Culture and Heritage,
Government of Nunavut, for reviewing "Wind and Shadow."

6 5 4 3 2 1   Printed in Canada 139   16 17 18 19 20

Writing books, in some ways, is a lot like parenting children. They keep you up through the night, your house is never clean and it takes a village to raise them.

When I married my wife, Colleen, my village grew, and I'm so fortunate that it did. I couldn't have written this book without the help of my parents-in-law: Carol, David and Georgette. And George too.

INTRODUCTION

Sometimes a surreal coincidence can be as creepy as hearing — or even seeing — something that goes bump in the night.

When I began writing this book, I had no idea one of the previous books in the series, *Haunted Canada 4*, would be nominated for the Hackmatack Children's Choice Book Award. Receiving the nomination was an incredible honour, and I was invited to tour New Brunswick for a week in April 2016. I decided that it would be fun to give kids in the schools and libraries I visited a sneak peek at *Haunted Canada 6* by sharing a New Brunswick story before it was published. Luckily, one of the stories in this book is set in Moncton, one of the cities I was scheduled to visit. A coincidence, to be sure, but a good one.

Or so I thought at the time.

The story "Where the Dead Take Centre Stage" shares the experiences of Capitol Theatre staff and theatregoers who have had blood-chilling encounters with the ghost of volunteer firefighter Alexander "Sandy" Lindsay. People have not only heard and sensed Alexander's presence in the theatre, but some have felt him grab them from behind.

Feel free to jump ahead and read that story now, then come back. I'll wait.

Shortly before I flew to New Brunswick, I found out where the Hackmatack Award ceremony would be held. And if you guessed the Capitol Theatre, you'd be right.

I was simultaneously delighted and horrified. What if I came face to face with the ghost backstage before the ceremony? What if some unseen presence grabbed me while I was giving my opening talk? Public speaking can be scary enough without adding paranormal activity into the mix.

My fear, it turned out, was for naught. At the end of an

incredible week that took me from Fredericton to Saint John to Moncton, and to many small towns in between, I entered the stunning, historic theatre and waited backstage with my fellow nominated authors. We laughed and shared stories and marvelled at the signed photographs of famous musicians and actors that covered the walls. But one thing we didn't do was see the ghost.

That's not to say that the ghost of Alexander didn't make his presence known.

Haunted Canada 4 was announced as the winning English non-fiction book, and I proudly took the stage to accept the award. As I said some thank-yous and briefly shared the haunted history of the theatre, a PowerPoint slide show projected the covers of the nominated books on a screen behind me. After the ceremony, I was informed by the event organizers that two of the book covers disappeared from the slide show, but they were still there when the file was later reviewed. Naturally the ghost received the blame for this unexplained occurrence.

Believe what you will, but I like to believe that the ghost did play a part in the missing images. Life's more exciting when you believe in the surreal.

If you agree, you're in luck. Between these pages you'll find true tales of haunted houses, macabre museums and chilling countryside. You'll encounter poltergeists, a possessed doll and a really nasty swamp hag.

And if you don't believe in ghosts yet, you might by the time you reach the end. But do yourself a favour: don't stay up too late reading. The surreal has a habit of becoming all too real as midnight approaches.

Frightfully yours,
Joel A. Sutherland

THE SWAMP HAG

Bell Island, Newfoundland and Labrador

The sun set on Bell Island's western horizon, casting a warm glow across the water and land. But a deep darkness descended swiftly, cold enough to chill your heart. A group of men, weary and exhausted from a full day's work in the mines, hurried to finish their farming chores.

Although work in the iron ore mines in 1943 was plentiful, the pay wasn't great, and some of the men had ten or more children. With so many mouths to feed and so little money to buy food, the men divided the fertile land of Dobbin's Garden and shared the work of growing and tending crops. Potatoes, carrots and cabbage filled their families' supper plates each night thanks to their efforts in the fields.

This night, as the men left one by one to return home

to their families, Nathaniel Hammond pressed on under the cover of darkness. He still had work to do with his potatoes, and he was so focused that he scarcely realized that he was now alone. He worked with his back to the large swamp that was surrounded by spruce trees and tall grass beside Dobbin's Garden.

With sweat coating his forehead and his muscles aching, his nostrils twitched and he detected an odd smell. It was a faint scent of rot, but it grew stronger with every passing second. He stopped working. The odour became so powerful and pungent that Nathaniel's head grew heavy, and he feared he might collapse.

He scanned the land, finally realizing he was the sole worker in the fields. But then he turned to look over his shoulder, and he saw her — a young woman. She had come out of the swamp and was approaching him slowly but deliberately. She wore a tattered and muddy white cloak that covered her head and concealed her face. Beneath the cloak she wore a dress that was covered in holes.

Nathaniel tried to call to her but couldn't even manage to say hello. It was the smell — it filled his mouth, coated his tongue and choked his lungs. It was like eating a rotten egg and washing it down with a mouthful of brackish swamp water. His stomach heaved and his legs suddenly buckled. Nathaniel fell to the ground, confused, disoriented and repulsed.

As he looked to the heavens above, the woman looked down upon him.

Unable to move, short of breath and utterly powerless, Nathaniel lay in the dirt as the woman crouched down at his feet, silently regarding him. The *thing* — that's how Nathaniel began to think of her, for he had decided she was no living woman — slowly crawled on her hands and knees up his body from his feet to his legs to his belly to his chest. Her head hovered mere inches above his. He closed his eyes. Greasy hair tangled with sticks, mud and decaying leaves brushed his nose and chin. Against his better judgment, but overcome with a powerful urge to look at his tormentor, Nathaniel opened his eyes and saw her face. He immediately regretted it.

Her skin was peeling off her skull. Holes covered her nose and cheeks, revealing bone and teeth. Her flesh was rotten and grey. But worst of all were the thing's eyes. Staring down at him with venom were two deep pools of darkness.

When she opened her mouth, her jaw bone cracked. And when she spoke, the nub of her decomposing tongue slithered like a slug in a mud puddle. Her stench was overpowering, so Nathaniel desperately tried to hold his breath.

"You heard me when I cried, pleaded and screamed for help," she hissed, "but you and your kind ignored my pleas. Because of you and your superstitious ways, I died a horrible death in that swamp. Now I have come back to avenge my own death!"

She lowered her face to his, so close that Nathaniel could practically taste the putrid swamp water that oozed from her pores. He gasped for air but couldn't breathe. The world grew darker than he thought possible, and stars danced before his eyes. Nathaniel whispered, "It wasn't me," and then lost consciousness.

Back home, Nathaniel's wife had grown alarmed when he hadn't returned with the other men. She looked for him at their neighbours' houses and discovered he was the last to remain in Dobbin's Garden. When the townsfolk learned Nathaniel was missing, a search party set out with lanterns in hand. They found Nathaniel lying on his back in a drill of potatoes. He wasn't moving, his clothes were covered in muck, and an awful smell wafted off his body. His brother John, who had joined the search party, was the first to kneel down beside Nathaniel. Fearing the worst, John was relieved to discover Nathaniel was still alive. They carried Nathaniel back to his house and called for the local doctor. Dr. Young's first words after arriving and laying eyes on Nathaniel were, "My God, did he fall into an outhouse?"

Nathaniel soon regained consciousness and told the assembled group what had happened to him. The smell, the attack, the woman — the thing. The doctor doubted the story, believing instead that Nathaniel had suffered a seizure and imagined the entire ghastly episode. But that didn't explain why Nathaniel smelled exactly like gassy swamp water. And since that day in 1943, more than two dozen men have been found in Dobbin's Garden, in the same dirty state, with the same story of a woman crawling out of the swamp and attacking them.

Some call her the Hag, others the Ghost of Dobbin's Garden. It's believed that, shortly before 1943, a young woman was picking berries alone when she ventured too far from home, became lost and called for help, but no one came to her rescue. She died in the swamp, alone and scared, cursing the locals who hadn't come to her aid. Fair or not, her vengeful ghost seems intent on terrifying as many Bell Island locals as possible.

Children are warned to stay far away from the swamp. Those who can't avoid Dobbin's Garden are warned to carry a Bible with them at all times. Even the bravest young men and women on the island know better than to be caught alone in Dobbin's Garden after sundown.

A SPINE-CHILLING READ

Barrie, Ontario

A woman stood alone in the cold, quiet night, waiting for a prescription to be filled at a pharmacy in the Wellington Plaza. Most of the shops in the strip mall were closed and empty, including Rivendell Books. Her gaze drifted as the minutes passed. And then she realized the plaza wasn't as deserted as she had thought. She noticed an elderly, grey-haired man in old-fashioned clothing who looked out of place walking back and forth in front of Rivendell Books. It was as if he was upset that the bookstore was closed and was searching for a way in. Then he found it: he approached the door and stepped straight through the glass.

The ghost of the old man is not unknown to the people who work at Rivendell Books. In fact, he might be one of their most loyal customers. He's certainly the most troublesome — frightening patrons as they walk up and down the aisles looking for their next read.

Wendy Cahill, the bookstore owner, has said that multiple odd and disturbing occurrences have taken place in the shop, often late at night when no one else is in the store. Many customers (*living* customers, that is) have seen the old man in the history section, and others have even felt him touch them before disappearing.

One day, while Cahill was in the back, she heard a loud bang in the front of the shop. She rushed through the store, puzzled by the sound and unsure what might have caused it. She found a biography about infamous serial killer Charles Manson lying in the middle of the floor. Someone had thrown it to the ground, but there was no one around. As Cahill stared, somewhat hypnotized, into Manson's cold eyes on the cover of the book, books started flying off the shelves and through the air around her.

Books flying off shelves is usually good for business, but Cahill found no comfort in the ghost's antics. She and her husband often stayed late on Saturday nights to clean and organize after the store had closed. No one else entered the store until the Cahills returned early on Sunday mornings. And yet when they made their way to the back the next day, they were regularly met by a disquieting sight. There, on the floor of the history section, were towers of neatly stacked books reaching high into the air. Most were about World War I and II.

It would be one thing if the ghost was content to remain in the store, but that's not always the case. One unfortunate customer purchased a book to read and enjoy, only to learn he had unwittingly invited a *bibliophantom* into his home.

Derek Ellis, a history buff, wanted to learn more about the Great War, so he browsed Rivendell Books' collection, completely unaware that the store he had entered was haunted. He selected a big book about World War I, paid for it and returned home. He had visited the store by himself, but he did not return home alone. Ellis would soon discover, in the middle of the night, that he had purchased a book that was one of the old ghost's personal favourites, and the spirit had no intention of missing a single night of reading.

A few minutes past midnight, Ellis suddenly woke up and came face to face with the ghost dressed in old-fashioned clothing. He was silently staring at Ellis from the foot of the bed, as if the ghost was angry at Ellis for having purchased the book from the shop. Ellis thought he might still be dreaming, but pinching his face and arms proved that he was awake and the ghost was real. The next day, Ellis did not tell his wife what he had seen for fear of scaring her, and he secretly hoped the midnight appearance would be the last he'd see of the bookstore ghost. It was not.

The next night he awoke after midnight again and smelled the strong aroma of flowers, despite the fact there were none in the room. Then, as he was trying to fall back asleep, a chair beside his bed creaked from the weight of someone sitting down on it. When Ellis rolled over and looked at the chair, it was empty. His cat then leaped onto

Inside Rivendell Books

the bed and stared intently at the empty chair as if sizing up some stranger. It left Ellis feeling very uncomfortable.

The midnight visits continued for the next few nights. On one occasion, Ellis awoke to see a bright red curtain that hadn't been there before, covering his closet door. After a few minutes the curtain suddenly disappeared.

Another night Ellis was woken by the sound of someone flipping through the pages of a book. He looked up and saw the old man standing in front of the closet. The ghost strode toward the bed, returned the World War I book to the nightstand, walked into the closet, waved to Ellis . . . and disappeared.

On the final night Ellis owned the book, he awoke once more to see the old man pacing the room, deep in thought while reading the book. The ghost wandered into the closet and disappeared again, and the book fell to the floor with a bang. Ellis had to retrieve it later.

Ellis began to fear that he was losing his mind, so as a final desperate measure, he took the book and visited a priest. The clergyman did not laugh or brush off Ellis's concerns. Far from it. With deadly urgency, the priest told Ellis he must get rid of the book, and in doing so get rid of the ghost.

Ellis followed the priest's advice and returned the tome of terror to Rivendell Books, but he didn't tell Cahill the real reason — the sinister reason — why he had decided to sell it back to the store. A month later, however, he returned and finally revealed the scary story. Ellis thought Cahill might not believe him, but she grabbed his arm and said, "My God! I do believe you." And then, in an ominous whisper, she added, "You wouldn't believe what's been going on in this shop."

In Rivendell Books, truth is often stranger — and scarier — than fiction.

DEMON HOTEL

Winnipeg, Manitoba

It was early October in 2012 and the first cool wisps of wintry air had begun to chill downtown Winnipeg's back alleys and shadowy corners. Crunchy, rust-coloured leaves swirled across the cracked pavement as the days grew shorter. A photographer and writer who calls himself Urban Explorer had passed by the Demon Hotel, an abandoned apartment building at 44 Hargrave Street, many times. Despite having felt compelled to enter the old building before, he had never built up the courage to do so. It had sat empty for many years, and most of the windows and doors were boarded up.

People who lived in the area had reported seeing pale, elongated faces with red eyes peering out from the few windows that hadn't been covered. It was widely believed that some of these entities were demons that had escaped from the underworld. With nervous laughter, locals often say, "when they're not in Hell, they stay at the Demon Hotel." Other people have spotted ghosts who try to plead for help, but when the spirits open their mouths, not a sound escapes . . . because their tongues have been ripped out from the backs of their throats.

Other locals recount the story of the spray paint that persists in appearing on one of the building's exterior walls. One day the words "DEMON HOTEL" were found painted on a sheet of wood that barred people from entering one of the broken doors. Fearing this ominous proclamation gave the neighbourhood an unsavoury appearance that would be bad for business, the local business association painted over it. Some time later, however, the words reappeared through the fresh coat of paint. More paint was applied to the wood, but once again the words came back. This happened time and again, defying all logic.

Since its construction in 1910, the apartment had seen more than its fair share of tragedy and death. A search of the newspaper archives reveals that in 1926 a resident of the building, Charles Seymour, was struck and killed by a streetcar when crossing Hargrave and Broadway. Seven years later, Mary Sue Burns ran out of the apartment and was killed by a passing Winnipeg Electric Company truck. In 1973, Lorraine Joan Bachinski was stabbed to death in the building.

Despite the bloody history and the all-too-apparent signs that something terribly evil dwelled there, Urban

Explorer could no longer resist the call to sneak in to take some pictures of the building's innards.

When no one was looking, he snuck inside as the sun was beginning to set. He slowly, hesitantly crept along a dark, dingy corridor. Paint was peeling off the walls and the floor was covered in dirt and debris. His nose was immediately assaulted by a revolting smell he described as equal parts decay and . . . something else . . . something not of this world. As he walked deeper into the belly of the building, the temperature dropped rapidly and it became unnaturally cold. He didn't hear any sounds other than his own heavy breathing and the scrape of his shoes, but that was about to change.

The broken and dust-covered stairs creaked loudly as he climbed them. It must have been his imagination, but he could have sworn that he was being watched as he neared the second floor. And then he heard a soft yet distinct sound: rustling in the room ahead. Remarkably, he carried on.

In the centre of the large room, he stopped. The pungent odour intensified. The air grew colder. The rustling became louder. He took a few pictures, and then something creaked above his head on the third floor. *The wind*, he tried to convince himself, *or an animal.* But no, it was no use trying to fool his mind. What he had heard was the unmistakable sound of soft footsteps passing over broken floorboards.

Although he nearly turned and fled, he forced himself to continue upwards. The footsteps above grew louder and more distinct as he quietly climbed to the top. But then

Demon Hotel

he accidentally kicked a broken piece of wood. It tumbled down the stairwell in a series of deafening bangs and crashes before it reached the bottom with a final, deadly crack. He froze. All was silent. Whatever he had heard on the third floor was no longer moving. Had it been his imagination?

Suddenly a door slammed on one of the lower levels, the sound echoing up the staircase. Fortunately he had spied a back stairwell — he had no intention of going back down the way he had come. He turned on his flashlight and made his precarious way down. He reached the main floor without incident, but as he peered a little farther down, into the basement, he felt a cold blast of air rush up from below. His flashlight flickered ominously. He should have left then and there, but some mad idea had taken shape in his head. He had come this far and seen nearly all of the Demon Hotel . . . all but the basement. He decided on a whim that he would go a little farther.

He went downstairs.

The nightmare basement was straight out of a horror movie: crumbling stone walls; rusted pipes, wires and hooks dangling from the low ceiling; dark holes in the floor and walls that might have held a hundred unseen terrors; ugly, unmentionable stains splattered in the corners.

After passing through a labyrinthine series of narrow halls and filthy rooms, he was overcome by an oppressive feeling of dread. He needed to get out immediately. He turned to backtrack out of the basement but quickly became disoriented and lost. His flashlight flickered once, twice and then shut off completely. The blackness pressed in on all sides and he couldn't see more than a few feet in any direction.

As Urban Explorer stumbled through the dark praying to find the exit, an evil aura suddenly filled the air, as strong and real as the cold. A spirit he described as "powerful and grotesque" slammed into his body, threw him against one of the crumbling stone walls and pinned his back against it. He fell to the ground and looked around wildly. His eyes landed upon his first stroke of good luck since he had bravely, perhaps foolishly, entered the Demon Hotel at dusk: the staircase was straight ahead. He picked himself up and ran as fast as his legs could carry him, up the stairs, out the door and into the night. He didn't stop running until he was far away. He never looked back.

In a bizarre, macabre twist, the Demon Hotel burned to the ground on April 6, 2015. The fire was blamed on teenage arsonists, but that hasn't stopped the locals from continuing to tell stories and to speculate as to what really happened on Hargrave Street. Many saw the faces and bodies of demons in pictures of the blaze that appeared on social media. Some believe the teens might have snuck into the building on an innocent dare but then became possessed by the spirits that lurked within and set fire to the building against their wills. Others were thankful to see the cursed building reduced to cinders and ash, but dreaded the possibility that the fire had released the ghosts into the city to find new homes. No one wants to think that the maze-like tunnels and rooms of the basement still sit beneath the earth, waiting for some unfortunate soul to discover them.

One thing is certain: the man who goes by the name Urban Explorer will forever wish that he hadn't explored the urban decay of the Demon Hotel.

WIND AND SHADOW

Nunavut

When snow and ice cover the ground as far as the eye can see, the world feels calm and tranquil. Perhaps even spiritual or supernatural. The sky swells with a cold, stony silence broken only by howls of wind. The land crunches and cracks underfoot. Every breath burns your lungs and your heartbeat (*ba-dum-ba-dum-ba-dum*) begins to slow its rhythm. *Ba-dum . . . ba-dum . . . ba . . . dum . . .*

When travelling alone across Nunavut, you might hear footsteps following behind you. You turn, but no one is there. An echo of your own footfalls? Perhaps. Then the sound of whispers flits past your left ear, your right. The wind? Possibly. Finally, voices and laughter jump out of the empty air right before your face, and now you're certain you're not alone.

It's possible you're walking with the *Taqriaqsuit*, also known as the shadow people, who fill the tales of Inuit mythology. These beings are rarely seen directly, but sometimes people catch a glimpse of one out of the corner of their eye: the outline of a face, a tangle of hair, a shadow upon the snow. The Taqriaqsuit, however, disappear into the ground as soon as they've been spotted or if they think humans sense their presence. Small blizzards follow at their heels as they walk across snow, covering their tracks and ensuring no one will know where they've been . . . or where they're going.

Some have heard the Taqriaqsuit but haven't seen any trace of them, such as George Agiaq Kappianaq's father. He used to go fishing with friends in a place called Kaaksaq. One night while camping, his group could hear the sound of people talking around them from sundown to sunrise. Others have also reported hearing laughter in Kaaksaq when no one else was nearby, which has been attributed to the Taqriaqsuit.

Some people have seen the Taqriaqsuit. Jolene Arreak recalls an account her grandfather told her about a man who once saw a group of Taqriaqsuit travelling across the snow on a dogsled. Instead of running the other way, this man jumped on the sled . . . then passed straight through it and landed on a patch of ice.

Nakasuk of the Nattilingmiut shares a story of an Inuk woman who spent time with the Taqriaqsuit and eventually married one. Over time, however, she grew increasingly frustrated by her inability to see her husband whenever she wanted. Out of frustration she picked up a knife and plunged it into the empty space of a chair where she believed he was sitting. Her assumption and aim were both true. Her husband suddenly materialized and fell from the chair to the floor, dead. The Taqriaqsuit wished to avenge their fallen but, fortunately for the Inuit who lived nearby, the shadow people did not attack. They did not feel it was fair to attack people who could not see them.

In Nunavut the winds screech and the shadows dance, and that's most likely what you're truly hearing and seeing: wind and shadow. But it's also possible that the Taqriaqsuit lurk nearby, moving, talking and watching.

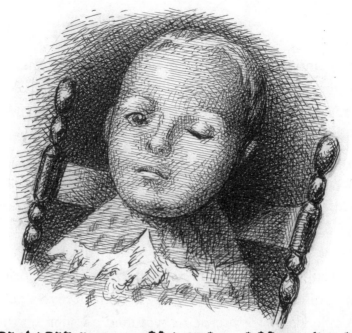

MUSEUM OF THE PARANORMAL

Niagara-on-the-Lake, Ontario

People come from all over the country — even from around the world — to see her. Day in and day out, she sits on a small, black rocking chair. The rocker, wreathed in shadow, is cornered away in the attic. She waits silently, her skin cracked and her eyes glassy, as people stare, ogle and point at her. Her name is Lizzie, and she's the prime attraction in the Museum of the Paranormal. Lizzie is a doll, but not the type you used to play with when you were younger. Lizzie is haunted.

Stephanie Cumerlato, who owns the museum with her husband, recalls the day Lizzie was donated to them. The previous owners were scared and agitated and needed to rid themselves of Lizzie's haunting presence. Their fear had reached an all-time high and they couldn't keep Lizzie in their house a single day longer. Every time they looked at Lizzie's oddly human face, Lizzie would look back . . . and then wink, as if sharing some sick, private joke.

Stephanie gladly accepted Lizzie and displayed her in the attic. Lizzie settled in and spent her days and nights with, among other attractions, Boris the (real, living) tarantula, a collection of authentic Ouija boards and the museum's collection of rare post-mortem photography. And yes, "post-mortem photography" is exactly what it sounds like: photographs of dead people, often from the Victorian era when families would take pictures of their deceased relatives.

People know they're being watched as soon as they set foot in the creaky attic. Lizzie's eyes follow visitors as if propelled by a dark, evil energy. One evening Stephanie was on the main level when a woman came down from the attic and said in a terrified hush that Lizzie had winked at her. An hour later, another woman entered the museum, climbed the stairs and returned looking as pale as a ghost. Although this second woman didn't know the first woman nor any of the stories surrounding Lizzie, she told Stephanie that Lizzie had winked at her too.

But ghostly goings-on were prevalent in the museum long before Lizzie moved in. The building, dating back to the 1920s, used to be a blacksmith's shop. Tragedy struck the business when the blacksmith's daughter stood too close to the fireplace. A spark flew out from the hearth and ignited the girl's dress in a roaring blaze. Despite attempts to save her life, the girl died. After the blacksmith passed away, people began seeing him and his daughter lingering in the building.

Lizzie in the Museum of the Paranormal

Today lights flicker on and off, faces peer out from the windows after the museum is locked up and the piano is often heard playing when no one is seated at it. One day a little boy pointed at the stairs and asked, "Who is that girl standing on the stairs?" No one else could see anyone there. Another time, a woman innocently told the Cumerlatos, "You know you have a ghost — she's standing beside the piano." Like the boy, the woman was the only person at the time who could see the forlorn ghost girl. A friend of Stephanie's was painting the staircase when a haunting face suddenly peered through the bannister with a sinister grin.

On another occasion, Stephanie's mother was helping her close the museum. It was late, they were all alone and it was pitch black. Stephanie remembered she had to feed Boris the tarantula some crickets, so they climbed up to the attic. After the task was done, they left Boris and Lizzie and made their way back down, but suddenly a powerful cold blast of air hit them head-on and Stephanie's mother gasped in fright. Stephanie assumed she had been startled by the inexplicable breeze. But that wasn't what had caused her fear. Her mother explained that someone had grabbed her hand and pinned it against the bannister. Stephanie then heard the disembodied voice of a young girl talking and laughing, as if the ghost was playing a practical joke.

One can only assume that Lizzie, sitting as still as a statue in the darkness above, might have winked in approval.

DON'T LET GO

Winnipeg, Manitoba

Everyone loves playing in the school playground during recess — everyone other than the children of St. Ignatius School. They avoid their school's rings at all costs. They know that to cross them is to cheat death or, more specifically, to cheat the girl who haunts their school's playground. And she's not a girl to be trifled with.

Not too long ago, a young boy approached the red rings with caution and a hint of fear. Although they weren't too high off the ground, a fall from that height coupled with an awkward landing could break a bone or twist an ankle.

A small crowd had formed around the boy to see if he'd make it across. He couldn't back down, not with so many eyes on him. The last thing the boy wanted was to be branded a coward, so he reached out a shaking, tentative hand and gripped the first ring. And then, swallowing his doubts and fears, he stepped off the ledge of the play structure, reached out his other hand and grabbed the second ring. Amazing even himself, he didn't fall. As he swung from ring to ring, his blood pumped harder and his smile grew wider. He was actually going to make it! But then, just when he reached the halfway point, someone grabbed his legs. He panicked and paused, struggling to hold on to the rings. The hands clawed up, up, up from his feet to his shins to his knees, pulling down as if trying to rip him free from the rings. The boy had to hold on with all his might and nearly lost his grip but, after summoning all his strength, was able to hang on tight and fend off whomever had tried to hurt him. He looked down and was shocked to see that there was no one beneath him.

Without wasting another second, the boy swung across the remaining rings and reached the safety of the other side. His friends were impressed and congratulated him for making it across, but he demanded to know who had tried to pull him down. His friends were dumbfounded. They hadn't seen anyone go near the boy.

Could the rumours be true? That was the only explanation the frightened boy and his equally frightened friends could think of. That a little ghost girl dwells on the playground with one simple mission in the afterlife: to pull children off the rings and to their deaths.

Legend has it that one day long ago, a kindergarten girl was attempting to cross the rings when her hand slipped and she fell. Tragically, her head struck one of the blue poles of the play structure with so much force that

Rings much like those at St. Ignatius School

she died before she hit the ground. Unwilling to leave the scene of her death, the little girl hides in the playground's shadows and waits — and watches. Filled with jealousy and seething with anger, she flies out of hiding and tries to pull others off the rings. But before anyone can get a good look at her, she disappears.

Opened in 1912 and run by the Sisters of the Holy Names of Jesus and Mary, the school has seen its fair share of challenges, from surviving the financial hardships of the Great Depression and the World Wars, to a 2007 electrical fire that burned down the oldest remaining wing of the building. But enrollment is high and the school is alive and well. Alive, except for the girl who would rather increase the playground's ghost population than see any children accomplish what she could not.

The children of St. Ignatius still warn each other to stay away from the red rings. And if someone is brave (or foolish) enough to try to cross them, the dire warning is clear and simple: whatever you do, don't let go.

AN IMAGINARY FRIEND

Montreal, Quebec

It's not uncommon for small children to have imaginary friends. When parents find their sons and daughters talking to an empty space, they know their child is simply going through a normal phase in life. There's certainly nothing unusual or creepy about it. Unless, of course, you one day begin to believe the supposed imaginary friend might not be imaginary after all — that the child is actually speaking and playing with someone from beyond the grave.

Newlyweds Kyle and Pete moved into their first home without any clue that something was amiss. It was the end unit of a row house on Georges-Vanier Street in Roxboro, a neighbourhood in Montreal. They were excited to start their married life together, and their heads were filled with dreams of what the future might hold. New experiences, new careers, children — it was very exhilarating. The house was admittedly small and ugly, but that didn't bother Kyle too much. It was all they could afford at the time, and she knew it wouldn't be their "forever home." But if she was being completely honest, there was something not quite right about the house on Georges-Vanier Street. Something she couldn't put her finger on. Even one of her best friends picked up on the bad vibe every time she visited. In fact, the friend hated coming over and told Kyle that she was certain there was some sort of presence in the house.

But life went on and they put such thoughts out of their minds. Soon they welcomed their first child, Gareth, into the world and brought him home. It was a happy time as Gareth grew and laughed and learned to crawl and walk and talk. And then, when Gareth was eighteen months old, something unusual began to happen.

Kyle found her son sitting on the bottom step of the staircase one day, looking up and talking to . . . something. Kyle looked upstairs, but no one was there. She asked Gareth who he was talking to.

"My friend," young Gareth replied. "Duke."

Kyle was surprised by the answer. Not only was this her son's first imaginary friend, but the name was unusual. Why Duke? They didn't know anyone named Duke and there weren't any Dukes in any of the books or shows they read and watched together.

The days passed and Gareth spent more and more time with Duke. "Come here, Duke," he would often say, leading his imaginary friend through the house. "Come with me, Duke." Often, when grown-ups would move to sit on the family room couch, Gareth would wave his arms wildly and yell, "Don't sit on Duke!" The bemused adults would willingly sit on the other side of the couch, looking at the empty spot beside them.

But was that spot actually as empty as the grown-ups believed? Kyle thought so, but her opinion would soon change.

One day while visiting with a neighbour who also lived on Georges-Vanier Street, Kyle casually mentioned that her son had an imaginary friend. As she elaborated and shared more details, her neighbour's eyes grew wider and wider. When Kyle revealed that the imaginary friend's name was Duke, her neighbour turned pale and finally spoke.

"Before you moved in, an old lady used to live in your home," the neighbour said softly with a slight quiver in her voice. "There was a fire. The old lady and her dog died in the blaze. The dog's name, Kyle. His name was Duke."

Everything suddenly made sense — bone-chilling, hair-raising sense. Gareth encouraging Duke to come down the stairs. Gareth patting his leg and telling Duke to "come with me." Gareth insisting that no one sit on Duke. His imaginary friend wasn't imaginary. He was a dog — a dead dog.

Gareth continued to talk and play with the ghost dog that only he could see until the day they moved out, when he was three years old. Gareth never saw Duke in their new house — the spirit had remained in the home where he had died — and Gareth never spoke of Duke again. In fact, now a grown-up, he no longer recalls having ever had an "imaginary" friend, ghost or no ghost. But his mother remembers only too well.

The next time you see a small child speaking to an empty corner of a room or an unoccupied chair, they might be playing with an imaginary friend. But it's also possible that the child might be making friends with an animal or person whose time on earth has come to an end, at least in the physical sense.

THE PIT OF DESPAIR

Dawson City, Yukon

The sky was grey and lifeless. The early morning sun was concealed behind a thick layer of clouds. The dirt road outside the Westminster Hotel was quiet. A figure walked alone.

The solitary figure was a mother who had come to see her son. He was a cleaner who worked the night shift at the Westminster Hotel. She walked slowly and hesitantly into the main floor lounge known as the Arm Pit and looked around. Not only was there no sign of her son, but she couldn't see another soul there. She called out. Her voice echoed across the room. No one replied. She slowly made her way deeper into the lounge. Then she heard something from the other side of the hotel.

The mother passed through a back passage that was

filled with dust, cobwebs and boilers, and approached a door to the bar, the Snake Pit. As she neared it, the sounds grew louder and became clearer. She could hear men's voices, talking, cajoling and laughing. And over the chatter was the distinctive clinking of poker chips. Had her son let his friends in for a game of cards when he was supposed to be working? The mother barged into the tavern and was met with the sight of another empty room. The sounds of the poker game, so clear when she was in the boiler room, stopped abruptly.

Wide, tall and painted baby pink, the Westminster Hotel has a bright and cheery face. But looks can be deceiving. Established in 1898 during the peak of the Klondike Gold Rush, the Pit, as locals affectionately call it, has seen its fair share of history.

Some of it has never left. Aaron Burnie, who works and lives in the Westminster Hotel, has witnessed no shortage of scary experiences he can't explain. He asserts that there is definitely "something" in the Pit, and he's not talking about the guests who visit the historic hotel to enjoy the rustic charm of its sloping ceilings and crooked floors. One night he awoke and needed to use the bathroom. All seemed normal until he made his way back to his room. Inexplicably, the hallway felt substantially colder, like he had entered a meat freezer. That gave him the creeps, but his next few experiences were far creepier.

After another trip to the second floor bathroom, Aaron was washing his hands when the locked door handle began rattling rapidly and loudly. Someone was trying to get in. "I'll just be a sec," Aaron called out. He quickly dried his hands, opened the door and found the hallway to be completely empty. Only three seconds had passed since someone had jiggled the handle. There was no possible way a living human being could have disappeared from the hallway so quickly.

Not long after, Aaron finally caught a glimpse of the ghost he had previously only felt and heard in the upstairs hallway — a man wearing a fedora hat, whom he'd see again and again, usually out of the corner of his eye. Others have seen him too, but that knowledge isn't necessarily comforting.

The spirit is protective of the lounge's piano. One day, when Aaron was relaxing in the Arm Pit, he saw a cellphone fly off the piano and across the room.

The Globe and Mail newspaper voted the Westminster Hotel the best venue in Canada for live music. If that's something you'd enjoy, you'll want to plan a visit soon. And if you prefer dead guests to live music, you also won't be disappointed.

TERMINUS OF THE DEAD

Vancouver, British Columbia

Experts believe that Waterfront Station might be the most haunted building in Vancouver, a city with such a bloody history that one of its streets is literally named Blood Alley. Built in 1915 by the Canadian Pacific Railway to serve the needs of a city that was growing rapidly, Waterfront Station was the Pacific terminus for trains travelling across the country from Montreal and Toronto. Since then, it has also become a terminus for the dead.

It's a grand building, built in a style reflective of the luxury and prestige that used to be synonymous with train travel. In its early days it contained accommodations for weary travellers as well as fine dining restaurants and a dance hall used for upper class parties and balls.

Today, some of these rooms are occupied by offices,

while others are used for storage, such as a room full of desks that have a habit of silently moving on their own.

On a dark, cold night, a security guard working the night shift prowled through the wide, empty halls of Waterfront Station. His footfalls echoed off the stone walls as he swung his flashlight from side to side. He was alone, or so he thought, as he entered one of the building's storage rooms. In order to search the room he had to swivel his large frame around the old desks that were stored there. When the guard reached the back of the room, he turned and was paralyzed with fear. The desks had silently floated off the ground and repositioned themselves. Some blocked the door while others were piled in the middle of the floor, forming a crude blockade that had cut him off from his only means of escape. Not only was he trapped, but he couldn't comprehend how that had happened.

There was only one explanation: the ghostly tales of Waterfront Station his co-workers had shared were true. A ghost — or perhaps a host of ghosts — had ensnared him in the room. But for what purpose? The security guard didn't wait around to find out. He ran full speed toward the desks, leapt up on the nearest one and sprinted across them to the door, eager to put the haunted room as far behind him as quickly as possible.

Between 2004 and 2005, a guard heard phantom footsteps in a stairwell on three separate occasions. The first time it happened the feet approached so quickly and unexpectedly that the guard barely had time to think before the sound ran past within half a metre of him. The second time he was a little more prepared and stood

Waterfront Station

in mute horror as the sound of someone running passed by, once again without a visible body. The third time the guard was not alone. He was with a colleague who also heard the footsteps, proving to him that the sound was not a product of his imagination.

One night, a different guard wandered toward the west side of the building where the dance hall used to be located. As he got closer, he slowed his pace. He heard something. It was faint at first, but it grew louder as he approached. It was the sound of music from the 1920s. That didn't make sense; the station's sound system wasn't connected. When the guard finally entered the old ballroom the music was so loud he thought he had just stepped back in time and into the middle of a swinging party. At first the room appeared to be empty. But then, out of the corner of his eye, he spotted a solitary figure: a woman, dressed in a 1920s flapper dress, waltzing alone across the floor in time with the music. The guard took a step toward the woman, but suddenly the music stopped and the woman vanished on the spot.

On another occasion, a guard opened a door and walked into a dark storage room, completely unprepared to come face to face with the old woman staring back at him. She glowed bright white and had a look of sadness and pain etched upon her face. The woman floated and reached her hand out to him, which sent him running in the opposite direction.

Others have also rounded a corner to find three women sitting on a bench as if waiting for a midnight train. Like the dancing spectre, they disappear almost as soon as they've been spotted.

And it's not only security guards who have seen ghosts in Waterfront Station. Many employees who work in the offices have had their fair share of unwanted paranormal encounters. Debra Lummas, a senior account executive, recalls the time she was speaking with another employee in one of the bathrooms when a third woman suddenly and creepily joined them. The stranger had wavy brown hair that flowed over her shoulders and wore a glamorous blue blouse from a different time period. She stared silently at Debra for an awkward ten seconds, then whispered in an ethereal voice, "I'll come back another time," and promptly vanished.

And finally, no account of the spirits of Waterfront Station would be complete without the Headless Brakeman who has been seen prowling on the tracks. On a night in 1928, as the rain was coming down in sheets, an unfortunate CPR brakeman named Hub Clark was working outside when he slipped and landed on his head. The fall rendered him unconscious and he lay sprawled across the tracks. A passenger train sped toward him before Clark regained consciousness, and he didn't see it coming. His head was cut clean from his body. It wasn't long before other CPR employees began seeing Clark step out of the shadows on misty nights, a lantern held high in the air. He walks up and down the tracks through the dead hours, forever searching for his missing head.

Last stop, Waterfront Station. End of the line. It's time to get off the train. But if it's late and you have a bad feeling in your gut, no one would blame you for wanting to stay on the train a little longer. Some of Waterfront Station's travellers have yet to reach their final destination.

THE LiViNG MUSEUM

Edmonton, Alberta

The Karpetz family purchased a beautiful home on Saskatchewan Drive and decided to spruce it up a little before moving in. Named the Firkins House after the original owner, it was well known to neighbours as the dwelling of some dark presence. But the Karpetzes had no idea. Soon — very soon — they would.

Shortly after taking possession of the possessed house, Audrey Karpetz worked late into the night painting one of the upstairs bedrooms. However, the spirit that inhabited the home's walls must not have appreciated the change in decor. Exhausted but satisfied with the day's work, Audrey, alone in the house, switched off the upstairs light and turned to leave. As she approached the top of the stairs, she was suddenly grabbed from behind in a tight and frigid embrace. She fought free from whatever had latched on to her body and ran outside as quickly as she could.

When she found the courage to look back at the house, she saw that the upstairs lights had turned back on. The rational part of her brain calmed her fears and reminded her that she had been alone. The logical explanation was that her mind was playing tricks on her. She must have imagined the touch of the hands and accidentally left the lights on in her haste to get out. She must have.

Filled with newfound (but slightly shaky) confidence, Audrey walked back into the house and up the stairs. She switched off the light and turned to leave.

Something grabbed her from the darkness, just as before.

This time, Audrey didn't try to convince herself it was only her imagination. The embrace of the hands was far too real. She screamed and ran out of the house. Once outside she saw that, much to her horror, the upstairs light had once again turned back on. She locked the door and left. Upon returning the next morning, Audrey and her husband Rod found that the upstairs light had been turned off at some point during the night.

The Karpetzes still moved into the house as planned, hoping the ghostly encounters would stop. They didn't.

Late one night, Audrey returned home with her two young daughters. She tucked the sleeping girls into their beds and went downstairs to the kitchen. There, sitting at the table like he owned the place, was an old man she didn't recognize. After overcoming her initial fright,

Audrey asked the man what he was doing in her house. She assumed he must be a friend of her husband's or a neighbour she hadn't yet had the opportunity to meet, but the man didn't answer. She rubbed her eyes and when she looked at the table again the man had disappeared without a trace.

In 1992, Rod and Audrey Karpetz sold the house, and it was transported to the Fort Edmonton Park, Canada's largest living museum. Located along the North Saskatchewan River, the park takes visitors through time, from the Fur Trade Era, the Settlement Era, the Municipal Era to the Metropolitan Era. Throughout the summer, the park is filled with costumed historical interpreters who interact with visitors, and for a once-in-a-lifetime experience the Hotel Selkirk is fully operational, allowing people to stay in the park overnight.

The legend of the haunted house in the living museum has grown over the years, making it hard to decipher the truth. People have reported seeing a transparent woman floating near a bookcase in the study, even claiming to have captured her in pictures. Others tell the story of a previous owner who repeatedly found a creepy ventriloquist's doll that turned up in odd places throughout the house as if it had a life of its own. Listen closely in one of the upstairs bedrooms that used to be a nursery and you might hear a disembodied voice singing lullabies as if to soothe a baby. And many people have reported seeing a boy running through the halls, bouncing a red ball in such a carefree manner that it seems he doesn't even know he's dead. There are so many reputable people who

Interior of the Firkins House

have seen odd phenomena that the reports are impossible to ignore.

Take, for example, the workers who were tasked with the building's restoration and installation in Fort Edmonton Park. Their tools kept disappearing and reappearing in bizarre spots as if they had grown legs. A windowpane flew out of a second-floor window frame and, despite being glass, didn't shatter or crack when it hit the ground below. It seemed like it had been guided softly down to the ground. It made no sense.

A security guard who worked the night shift in the park for years had countless odd experiences when he was, presumably, all alone. He says that once the spirits got to know him he was mostly left alone. His two most vivid (and chilling) memories from within the Firkins House include one night when he saw a chair slide from one side of a room to the other, and another night when he was pushed violently from behind.

Have you decided whether or not you'd want to spend a night in the Hotel Selkirk, so close to the Firkins House? Well, before you book a room, consider this. A tourist who stayed overnight wandered through the park after it had closed and filmed the historic buildings. Nothing seemed out of the ordinary . . . at the time. But when he reviewed the footage a few days after his trip, he couldn't believe what he had captured. The video showed that he was alone in the middle of the moonlit street. The camera was focused on the Firkins House. And then a faint voice clearly whispered, *"Come see . . ."* followed by the piercing squawk of a crow.

The choice is yours. Visit Fort Edmonton Park during the day, or spend a night sleeping beside one of the country's most haunted houses. It's sure to be a night you'll never forget.

THE CRISIS APPARITION

Sydney, Nova Scotia

Winter came early to the colony of Cape Breton Island in 1785. It was October 15, yet Sydney Harbour was already frozen, delaying the delivery from England of much needed supplies that the 33rd Regiment of Foot were expecting. The British soldiers were holed up in their barracks as snow piled up outside their doors and their windows froze over with crackling ice.

The men were prisoners to the severe weather and passed their time playing cards and trying not to succumb to the madness of cabin fever and isolation that threatened to crush them under its weight. It was in the midst of this dire situation that Captain John Coape Sherbrooke would look upon the face of his friend, Lieutenant George West Wynyard, and become filled with dread. "I have heard,"

Sherbrooke would later remark, "of a man's being as pale as death, but I never saw a living face assume the appearance of a corpse, except Wynyard's at that moment."

On the night in question, between 8 and 9 p.m., Sherbrooke and Wynyard sat before a warm fire discussing literature and ideologies while drinking coffee. They weren't interested in gambling nor were they alcohol drinkers, so they spent many evenings in Wynyard's parlour, apart from the other soldiers. There were only two doors in the sitting room: one leading to the barracks's hallway and the other to Wynyard's bedroom. As they passed the time in conversation, Sherbrooke happened to glance at the doorway that led to the hall. Standing in it was a man he had never seen before.

This man was young and tall but looked very ill. He was as pale as frost and emaciated, looking as if he hadn't eaten in days, or even weeks. The mysterious man was not dressed in a military uniform but in a hunting suit. He held a whip in his hand.

Sherbrooke alerted Wynyard to the stranger. As soon as Wynyard laid eyes on the intruder he became incredibly agitated and his face took on the appearance of a corpse, as Sherbrooke would later describe. Wynyard couldn't move, couldn't speak. So the two men looked at the third in stony silence. Finally, after an uncomfortable pause that felt like a lifetime, the stranger crossed the room, looked at Wynyard with deep sadness and pain, and then walked into the bedroom, out of sight.

Wynyard drew in a gasp of air as if he hadn't breathed for a few minutes — in truth, he probably hadn't — and then grasped Sherbrooke's arm. "Great God!" he exclaimed. "My brother!" As far as Wynyard was aware, his brother Jack was home in England.

Failing to understand how Wynyard's brother could be in Cape Breton, and certain Wynyard must be mistaken, Sherbrooke led his friend into the bedroom to ask the stranger who he was. But the small room — including the closet — was completely empty. *Impossible,* Sherbrooke thought. There were no other doors and the windows were sealed shut with ice. The men took their search back into the parlour and even examined the hallway but found no trace of Wynyard's brother. He had disappeared. They took note of the time at which the emaciated man had first appeared and made a pact not to tell any of the other men for fear of creating a stir.

But Wynyard was distraught. He thought that something bad had happened, that some tragedy had befallen his brother, and that the haunting vision that had walked through his sitting room was a bad omen.

Time passed but his anxiety did not. He grew increasingly impatient for the next shipment of letters from England, hoping to hear his brother was okay, and he began to confide in his comrades that he feared his brother might not be well. The other men in the 33rd Regiment became suspicious. Finally, after prolonged prodding, Wynyard shared the story of his brother's appearance in the night.

The men quickly became obsessed with the tale and were determined — perhaps nearly as much as Wynyard himself — to discover what had happened. They searched newspapers from England for any notice of the Wynyard name and anxiously awaited the next delivery of letters from home. When the mail finally arrived, all the men demanded to know if Wynyard had received a letter before they asked for their own long-awaited correspondence from home. But no letter had come for Wynyard. The men, disappointed, dispersed.

There was, however, a solitary letter addressed to Sherbrooke. He stood staring at it for some time and then finally turned it over, broke the seal and opened it. After a quick glance at its contents, Sherbrooke asked Wynyard to follow him to a private room. They left.

Silence filled the mailroom. The soldiers were convinced Sherbrooke's letter contained some clue — perhaps the full explanation — to the appearance of Wynyard's brother earlier in the year.

After an hour had passed and the suspense had become nearly unbearable, Sherbrooke finally returned. He crossed the room without speaking or making eye con-

New settlement on the Island of Cape Breton, 1785

tact with anyone and stopped at the fireplace. He rested his arm and head on the mantel and stared deep into the flames. After another agonizingly drawn-out moment, he said in a low whisper that only those closest to him could hear, "Wynyard's brother is no more."

The letter had begun: "Dear John, Break to your friend, Wynyard, the death of his favourite brother." It further explained, Sherbrooke relayed with a chill, that Jack had died on October 15 at the exact time that the ghost — for by now the men had come to believe that the emaciated stranger must surely have been a ghost — had walked into Wynyard's parlour and looked forlornly at his brother.

But Jack Wynyard was no simple ghost. He was what's known as a crisis apparition — the spirit of a person who appears before loved ones at the time of death.

Why Jack's spirit travelled halfway around the world and walked past his brother without a word before disappearing is unknown. But forty years later, while speaking with a friend, Sherbrooke solemnly swore that the story was completely true. That night had made him a changed man who looked on matters of life, death and eternity in a different light, and he believed he'd soon be called into another world himself. Whether or not he returned after death is unknown.

AFRAID OF THE DARKE

Regina, Saskatchewan

In the late 1800s, Francis Nicholson Darke was a success-
ful businessman and landowner. He was also mayor of
Regina, a member of parliament and donated much of the
money needed to build the University of Regina. As a sup-
porter of the performing arts, he funded the construction
of the Darke Hall for Music and Art on the campus. He
died in 1940, but that hasn't stopped him from enjoying
the performances in the building named for him.

During musical programs, modern-day audiences have
spotted a man sitting in the middle of the auditorium who
stands out from the crowd. He's well dressed in a suit that
resembles the style that was popular in the early 1900s,
and he always sits alone. He doesn't speak to anyone
nor seem to even be aware of his surroundings, utterly

Francis Nicholson Darke (back row, second from right)
Regina Town Council, 1896

transfixed by the music performed on stage. When the music ends and the audience stands to applaud, the man disappears.

Darke has also been seen in other locations about campus. Dana Hryhoriw, who would later form a paranormal research team, saw her first ghost standing on the steps outside Darke Hall. She locked eyes with the man and immediately felt like a thousand volts of electricity had surged through her body and taken her breath away. Wanting to learn more about whom the man might have been, she went to the library and began flipping through the pages of local history books. She turned to a picture of Darke from the 1930s and knew at once it was the man she had seen. It was as if he was looking out at her intently from within the picture.

Terry Duckett, a technician with the university's music department, recalls with uneasiness an odd occurrence that took place every night for three weeks. Whenever he was alone in the evening he felt a powerful draft of cold air pouring down from the ceiling near his office. There were no vents nearby and he checked to make sure all the building's doors and windows were closed. Finally, things grew too scary for Terry and — although he doesn't know why — he said, "Good night, Frank," as he was locking up. The cold air immediately turned to warm air, and Terry ran from the building.

Are you afraid of the dark? If one day you enroll for classes at the University of Regina, you might be wise to develop a healthy fear of the Darke.

THE HAUNTING OF HILLCREST HOUSE

St. Catharines, Ontario

It's a beautiful home on an idyllic street in Ontario's historic Garden City. But beauty can be deceiving, and something dark and sinister dwells within the house on Hillcrest Avenue.

Lindsay was a teenager when her family moved in. With many windows, white pillars and a red door, the home had a pleasant, welcoming face. Large, mature trees grew on the property and green bushes filled the garden, creating a warm and healthy appearance that made the house instantly feel like home.

Once they had unpacked, Lindsay, her sister and their two brothers began exploring every nook and cranny. One of the house's interesting quirks was the attic. It wasn't the type you'd see in a horror movie, with dust-covered knick-knacks and cobwebs in every corner. Instead, it was a finished and functional living space with a sitting room at one end and a bedroom at the other. Lindsay and her siblings discovered that there was a secret passage joining the sitting room and bedroom. It was exciting and mysterious, but it also felt . . . wrong. Lindsay had the feeling that she was being watched in the attic, whether she was with her siblings or alone. With the sickening sensation of eyes on her back, she'd spin around — but nothing was ever there.

The secret tunnel also had a secret of its own. Set into one of the walls was a hidden cubbyhole that the kids stumbled upon one day. They opened it, reached into the darkness and pulled out, much to their surprise, a German army helmet from the World War I era. Called a *pickelhaube,* the helmet was made of black polished leather and had a large metal spike sticking straight up from its top. Lindsay and her siblings were filled with curiosity and a touch of fear as they passed the spiked helmet among them, wondering what horrors the helmet had seen. And how had it ended up in a hidden cubbyhole, in a secret tunnel, in the attic of their home? They returned the helmet to its hiding place and tried to put it out of their minds.

But as strange and creepy as the attic was, nothing could match the feeling of fear that filled the house's library on the main floor.

It was a long room situated in the back of the house and running the entire length of the main floor. The family filled it with books and cozy wing chairs perfect for reading. Their television sat in a corner, and it was their preferred room for socializing and relaxing. But Lindsay's sister admitted that she felt like she was always being watched by an unseen presence in the library, just as Lindsay had felt in the attic. That didn't keep them out of the room, but it did stop several dogs from entering. Oddly, no dog ever set foot in the library. Instead, they put on their brakes and went ramrod straight outside the room's doorway. With bristling hair and bared teeth, the dogs whined incessantly, a pitiful sound of terror and agitation. The dogs' instincts were clear: there was something bad in the library, whether the humans could see it or not.

Early one morning, Lindsay's mother woke up and walked downstairs. She was often the first person in the household to rise, and she passed from room to room tidying and getting ready for the day. The house was silent, empty. Nothing seemed unusual or out of place, until she entered the library.

All of the books had been taken down from the shelves and were laid out on the floor in the shape of a star. Wondering who had created the mess, she picked up the books and returned them to the shelves. She might have forgotten the unusual occurrence had it been an isolated event, but it happened again. Another morning she came down to find the books on the floor in the shape of the letter H. Again she cleaned them up thinking that would be the last time, but she found them another morning arranged in a series of large squares, and a few days later in perfectly spaced rows.

She was convinced that the children were playing a

practical joke on her, sneaking downstairs in the dark to lay out all the books, but each child insisted she or he was not to blame. Possessing the uncanny ability mothers have to know immediately when one of her children is telling a lie, she knew that her kids were telling the truth. But the books continued to move during the night and form perfect geometrical patterns on the floor.

Despite the dogs' refusal to enter the room and a shared and growing feeling amongst the family that the library was haunted, no one saw or felt a presence within. That was about to change.

Late one night, Lindsay was home alone. The house was dark. Every sound — the wind blowing a tree branch against a window, the tick-tock of an old clock, the creaks and groans of the wood floors — was amplified by the silence. Lindsay decided to sit and rest in one of the library's wing chairs, a choice she'd soon regret. An eerie sensation washed over Lindsay, and goosebumps prickled her skin. With a sickening lurch in her stomach, she suddenly believed there was someone directly behind her. She turned swiftly and looked over her shoulder, but no one was in the space between her chair and the wall.

She turned back around, but before another second passed a hand grabbed her left shoulder from behind. She tensed and froze, her breath catching in the back of her throat. Lindsay could make out the distinct feeling of four fingers and a thumb on her flesh and bone. It was not a comforting pat, the sort of gesture a loved one would give. It was something evil, something cruel. After a short moment that felt like an eternity, the hand pressed down on her hard, pinning her to the chair. And then, as suddenly as it had touched her, it let go. Lindsay turned again but saw only her own reflection in a window looking back at her. She screamed, leapt out of the chair and ran out of the library. She sought out the company and security of her dogs, went into the kitchen and turned on the radio for a distraction as she waited for her family to return.

Many years have passed since Lindsay and her family moved out of Hillcrest House, but they'll never forget the *pickelhaube,* the mystery of the rearranging books and the hand that squeezed Lindsay's shoulder one night. Memories may fade, but fear is forever.

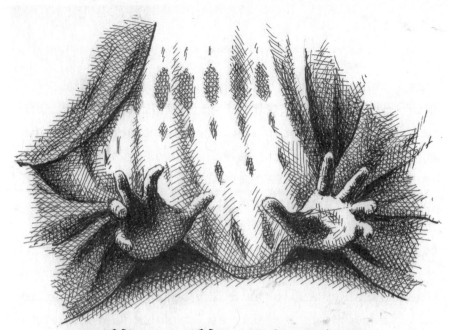

WHERE THE DEAD TAKE CENTRE STAGE

Moncton, New Brunswick

The historic Capitol Theatre has a 782-seat auditorium, but one of those seats is spoken for. Permanently.

In 2014, Lindsay Isenor and a few friends took a tour of the theatre, which has been designated as a Provincial Historic Site. When she stepped onto the stage and took in the decadent beauty of the two-storey auditorium her jaw dropped. She was speechless. Although this emotional reaction was completely natural given the splendor of the theatre, she would soon experience similarly intense reactions created by decidedly unnatural forces.

Lindsay's tour of the Capitol included a stop in the lobby where she saw an old black and white photograph of Alexander "Sandy" Lindsay. Below Alexander's picture was a plaque that told his tragic story. On March 26, 1926, a fire devastated the Capitol and the Empress, a theatre next door. Alexander, a volunteer firefighter, rushed into the Capitol to fight the blaze. He was in the basement when the stage collapsed, crushing him beneath the rubble. To this day he remains the only on-duty firefighter to have lost his life in Moncton. He also remains, according to present-day staff, the theatre's resident ghost.

After Lindsay and the tour group crossed the catwalk above the stage and saw the original brick walls that are still charred from the fire, an employee told the group about a frightening vision he'd witnessed late one night. He had looked up and spotted a man walking across the balcony. That was alarming enough since no one else was supposed to have been in the theatre. The truly scary part was that the stranger was not bothering to walk *around* the seats, but was walking straight *through* them.

Feeling excited and a little anxious from this story, Lindsay and her friend Dave investigated the balcony alone. They sat in one of the rows and waited, hoping to experience their own fright. They soon got their wish.

One of the seats directly behind them began to squeak as if someone seated there was moving side to side to get a better view of the stage. They spun around, but all of the chairs were empty. Then, from the same empty seat where they had heard movement, a man began to laugh. Whether the ghost was laughing at a performance only he could see or at the startled looks on Lindsay and Dave's faces, no one could say. But they were determined to find out who the ghost was, so they asked, "What is your name?"

"Alex," said a gruff, moaning voice.

Lindsay and Dave confirmed that they had both heard the ghostly response, and then a whistle sounded three times from the stage — *fweet, fweet, fweet* — as if in reply to Alex's voice.

Later, when Lindsay and Dave rejoined their friends, Charmian and Dwayne, they asked if anyone on the main level had whistled. No one had.

The group agreed they could all use a break. While they sat on the stage and chatted, Lindsay noticed that a door she had propped open and secured with a stop wedge was now closed. She asked if anyone had closed the door. Everyone shook their heads. She rewound through the footage on a camera that she had set up on a tripod onstage. The open door could be seen in the back of the frame. With the soft blue light of the camera's screen illuminating her face, Lindsay watched the odd scene in horror: a moment after the group passed through the doorway, the stop wedge flew out from under the door. The door swung shut, missing the last person in the party by mere inches, but somehow didn't make a sound. It was like a scene out of a horror movie, and the friends had unwittingly become the terrorized characters.

Charmian and Dwayne, sensing that the paranormal activity in the theatre was growing in intensity, ventured into the basement where the collapsed stage had claimed Alexander's life many years ago. A short while later, Dwayne fled from the basement and rejoined the others. They could tell something was bothering him and asked what had happened. He told them that he and Charmian had brought along an Ovilus, a device that reads electro-magnetic frequencies and changes in temperature, then feeds the data into a preset database of over two thousand words, allowing spirits to communicate with the living. When they turned on the Ovilus three words came through:

Bury

Under

Burn

The temperature then immediately plummeted and Dwayne was overwhelmed with an odd sense of dark energy, forcing him to leave.

It's clear that Lindsay and her friends were joined by the ghost of Alexander that night. But for them, it was an isolated event. For the Capitol's staff, working with the spirit is an all-too-familiar aspect of the job.

Kimberley Rayworth, Development Director at the theatre, says that almost every member of staff has felt Al's presence, including her.

It was Christmas day, and all was quiet and calm. Although the theatre was closed, someone had to stop by the empty building to make sure the pipes hadn't frozen. That someone was Kim. Luckily she didn't have to go in alone. She happened to be dog-sitting for one of the theatre's regular performers, so she took Norman the dog along with her for company.

Kim and Norman walked through the quiet building, the sound of their feet and paws echoing in the empty rooms. All seemed well. No frozen pipes, no other emergencies. She was almost ready to lock up and return home

Stage in the Capitol Theatre

when something unexpected and unsettling happened.

They were in a conference room located under the second floor balcony — under Alexander's seat. Without warning, an awful feeling of not being alone overwhelmed Kim. Norman grew really quiet and dropped uncomfortably low to the ground. Suddenly, the silence was shattered by the sound of heavy fireman's boots running across the floor above her head. The hair on her arms and neck stood on end and her body grew painfully cold. Kim's mind went instantly to Alexander — somehow, she knew he was in the building with her, perhaps looking for a little company over the holidays.

Julie Pallot, the theatre's Guest Services Manager, was leading a tour for a local class of ten- to twelve-year-old students when she had her own paranormal experience. She led the kids to the stage and stood with her back to the curtain while she shared the theatre's history and told them about the resident ghost. As Julie began to suspect that the kids didn't really believe a spirit haunted the old building, a teacher standing beside her on the stage suddenly screamed loudly. The teacher clamped her mouth shut and didn't say what had scared her, but her face was pale and a look of fear had overcome her. She looked like she had seen a ghost. As Julie would soon find out, the teacher hadn't seen a ghost — she had *felt* one.

Not wanting to embarrass the teacher in front of the students, Julie waited until they were alone before she asked what had happened. With a pinched mouth, a shake of her head and a look of repulsion, the teacher said that while Julie spoke to the class, someone had grabbed her leg from behind. And then fingers had squeezed her tightly.

There hadn't been anyone near them — no one *living*, that is. To this day, Julie never stands in front of the curtain while speaking to groups. She sits on the edge of the stage, a safe distance from the curtain. She has no desire to be grabbed by a cold, dead hand.

In the Capitol Theatre there are two types of shows that take place on its historic stage: live performances and dead ones.

GHOST HiLL

Luskville, Quebec

In the 1940s, a farmer named Wyman McKechnie was out walking under a large moon in a clouded sky. Whenever the clouds blew in front of the moon McKechnie found it difficult to see much further than a few feet, but when the clouds parted he happened to look over his shoulder. There, standing in the middle of the road on Ghost Hill, was the shadowy shape of a man in a white cloak, floating a foot above the ground. Terrified, McKechnie yelled and quickened his pace. The ghost behind matched his speed. McKechnie broke out into a run and the ghost followed suit. McKechnie sprinted but still he couldn't lose his pursuer. He ran until he was forced to sit on a log to catch his breath.

The ghost glided to the other end of the log and said in a whisper, "Well, we were certainly going some there."

McKechnie jumped to his feet and found the courage to respond, "Yes! And now that I've got my breath we'll go some more!" He beat the ghost back to his home, but he couldn't outrun the nightmares that plagued his sleep thereafter.

Today, Highway 148 runs through Luskville, up and over Ghost Hill. The only buildings on Ghost Hill are a small stone church that's built so close to the road it's practically in the middle of it, and an old farmhouse tucked out of sight on a hidden lane. The bush that grows on both sides of the road is tangled and oppressive, and the road itself is steep and winding. There have been many fatal accidents on this stretch of road over the years. Some blame the road. Others blame the ghosts.

In the early 1800s, a young man stalked silently through the woods with a shotgun in hand. He was hoping to catch a partridge or two for his evening meal. The sky was unnaturally dark and gloomy, casting a lifeless grey light on his surroundings that made it very difficult to see.

As the man began to climb a hill, he saw a cow at the top lumbering slowly down toward him. The man stopped and regarded the cow; it looked odd in the dying light. Something wasn't quite right. And then the cow suddenly began to charge the man, running in a very peculiar fashion. The man had a bad feeling in his gut. He raised his rifle and, when the cow had covered half the distance, he pulled the trigger. A loud bang echoed over the hills. The cow toppled over right beside an old, gnarled tree. The man ran to it and looked down in horror. The cow he thought he had shot turned out to be another man — his best friend, in fact — who had put on a cow's hide to frighten his buddy. It worked, all right. And the practical joker paid for the gag with his life.

But his soul could not pass on. It's believed his spirit left his still-warm body and fused into the tree. The branches looked like bony, many-fingered arms, the roots like knobbly legs stuck in the muck and the bark like the folded wrinkles of a face that has seen too much pain and misery. The hill where the tree stood became known as Ghost Hill.

The haunted tree wasn't content to become a forgotten part of the landscape. Instead, it became the source of much mischief, enacting revenge on unsuspecting and unfortunate travellers who happened by. Terrified farmers abandoned their wagons and rushed to the safety of their homes, telling their families that the wheels had seized in the middle of Ghost Hill as if some unseen force had reached out and ensnared them in its mighty grasp. Horses commonly became agitated and spooked, seemingly at nothing, and kicked up on their hind legs, dropping their drivers to the ground and bolting away in the night. Men who found themselves without a horse would get up, brush the dirt off their pants and suddenly hear eerie sounds like whispers that grew to howls in the woods all around them. No one stayed long to find out what made those uncanny noises in the dark.

Something had to be done about the haunted tree. And so, in 1830, the task of chopping it down fell to the man who owned the land, an Irish immigrant and farmer named Joseph Lusk.

Mad with fear and laughing hysterically, Joseph Lusk hacked away at the base of the gnarled tree. Lightning flashed and illuminated Lusk's wide eyes as he threw himself at his fevered task, pausing only briefly now and again to wipe sweat out of his eyes and brush wood chips off his coat. With every gouge he cut in the tree he could swear he heard an anguished scream. It was as if he wasn't chopping down a tree, but hacking a human to bits. In a dark, twisted sense, that wasn't too far from the truth.

Ghost Hill Farm

When the work was done, the townsfolk hoped they would no longer see another ghost. But a few short years later, Ghost Hill claimed another innocent victim.

A couple of men were returning home late at night from a tavern in nearby Aylmer when they broke out into an argument. The friends had fought before, as friends do, and their disagreements were normally resolved and quickly forgotten. This time, however, one of the men reached into the back of his horse-drawn wagon, pulled out a pitchfork and impaled his friend upon the metal prongs, right at the top of Ghost Hill. The murdered man's spirit took up permanent residence in the woods.

In 1885, a local farmer by the name of Jim Boyer had a profitable day at the Aylmer market, selling butter, pork and vegetables. He rode home happy, his pockets heavy with profits, when a band of robbers ambushed him on Ghost Hill, stole his money and left him to die in a puddle of his own blood. Boyer's soul joined the multiplying group of hilltop ghosts forever wailing for justice against their murderers but never finding peace.

It's believed other spirits skulk through the woods of Ghost Hill, and in the 1930s one of these ghosts hitched a ride on a bus as it drove along Highway 148. As the driver crested the hill, he happened to steal a glance in the rear-view mirror. He had thought the bus was empty, so he was shocked to see an elderly woman sitting in one of the back rows, looking solemnly out the window. As he drove down the other side of the hill, he wondered how he hadn't seen her get on the bus. He decided he should pull over at the bottom of the hill to let her out. As he passed a small cemetery he heard a loud *whoosh* — as if something had flown straight past him, through the closed door and out into the night. The driver stopped the bus, opened the door and turned around . . . but the bus was empty once again.

Sometimes a name is only a name, nothing more. But Ghost Hill is more than that. It's a dire warning of what you'll find if you're brave enough to venture through Luskville.

SPIRITS IN THE SANATORIUM

Fort Qu'Appelle, Saskatchewan

As the teenage musicians gathered outside the building where their summer band camp was being held, on the grounds of what was once the Fort Qu'Appelle Sanatorium, it suddenly dawned on one of the young men that he had forgotten something. But what? He had his case, his instrument . . . *My sheet music!* he suddenly remembered. He had left it in his room. He told his bandmates he'd return and raced back to their lodge alone. The boy ran up the stairs and into his room where he picked up his music . . . and paused.

He had heard something. He thought he was the only person currently in the building, which had been assigned to the boys. A soft, lilting voice was coming from the bathroom, singing beautifully. The voice clearly belonged to a woman.

As he hesitantly approached the bathroom, the woman's voice grew louder and clearer. It was accompanied by the sound of running water. He stood in the hallway for a moment, listening to the woman's song and building up the nerve to investigate further. Finally he cracked open the door.

The woman continued singing. Her back was to the boy. She wore a long, old-fashioned dress and was washing her hands in the sink as she sang.

With a dry swallow, the boy said, "Excuse me? Lady? I think you are in the wrong lodge."

She didn't stop singing, she didn't stop washing and she didn't acknowledge the boy in any way. It was as if she was in her own world. The boy would soon realize that she was, quite literally, in her own world — a parallel world.

But then she stopped singing abruptly and turned off the taps. She stood statue-still and didn't turn around. All he could see was her back. The sudden silence was deafening, nerve-wracking. Finally, she backed away from the sink and out of sight.

The boy stepped into the bathroom and looked around the corner, but it was empty. The woman had disappeared. He looked more closely at the sink. It was completely dry.

The boy knew he had seen a ghost singing and washing in the bathroom; the only question was which one? There is no shortage of spectres roaming Fort San's haunted halls.

The most well-known is Nurse Jane, a woman who is said to have become so distraught from treating hundreds of sick and dying patients that she ended her life. She's often seen in her white uniform and cap, wandering the halls pushing a squeaky, empty wheelchair, with a morose, downcast glance.

Others have seen the ghosts of children running through the buildings and outside in the woods, some laughing, some crying. Many have been woken in the middle of the night by the sounds of beds being dragged across the floor, chains rattling above, hushed voices in the dark, and windows and doors opening and closing on their own.

Fort Qu'Appelle Sanatorium, or Fort San, was opened on October 10, 1917, to treat patients with tuberculosis. At its peak as a tuberculosis sanatorium, Fort San was so large that it produced its own power and grew its own crops. It was virtually self-contained, with a school, canteen, barber shop, post office, movie theatre, library and internal radio station. It also had a morgue, of course. Unclaimed bodies were carted out of the main building and buried in unmarked graves in a small cemetery nestled in the woods.

As tuberculosis cases dwindled, so did the need for sanatoriums, and Fort San was closed on April 1, 1971. The property was then used as a summer school for the arts and a conference centre.

It's rumoured that years after the sanatorium closed the new owners discovered that the entrances to the tunnels that connected all of the buildings and the morgue had been sealed shut. They pried them open and were horrified to find hundreds of dried and shrivelled bodies underground. It's little wonder there are so many stories of ghostly encounters.

One night a man named Pat was trying to sleep when someone grabbed his hand and checked his wrist for a pulse. When Pat opened his eyes, he saw that his hand was raised in the air and there were finger indents on his skin. But no one stood beside him. The ghost finished checking Pat's vitals and placed his hand back down on his chest. Pat couldn't bear the thought of spending one more night there and left.

Since 2004 the buildings have sat unused, slowly crumbling and falling into disrepair. The fields are over-grown and the cemetery has been reclaimed by nature. This seems to please the spirits just fine.

A man named Dieter explored the abandoned proper-ty with three friends, two of whom grew too scared and had to wait outside one of the buildings. Dieter and the friend who remained with him searched every single room, from the top floors to the lowly basement. Once they were certain that they were the only living beings inside, they knocked on the walls and called upon spirits to knock back in response. A silent second passed, then another, a third and finally they heard a reply: *knock, knock, knock.* That was enough for Dieter and his friend, and they quick-ly ran out of the building. They rejoined their two friends outside, where they saw through the windows orb-like lights zipping up and down the halls. It was absolutely terrifying, and they ran off the property, never to return.

More recently, a woman took her Rottweiler-Doberman mix, a large and powerful dog she described as "afraid of nothing," to explore the abandoned sanatorium. As soon as they arrived, the dog ran through the main building's

Fort Qu'Appelle Sanatorium

open door. She waited outside for ten minutes, too afraid to move and hoping her dog would return. She couldn't hear the dog running or barking, and she finally grew too concerned to wait outside any longer. She walked in, up the stairs, down the hall and finally found the dog. He was alone in an empty room, standing ramrod straight, staring at an empty corner. He didn't respond when his name was called. Suddenly something imperceptible happened. The dog broke out of his trance-like state and ran out of the room, shooting past his owner in a blind panic. He tore around the building in a frenzy, running back and forth down halls, up and down the stairs and around and around in circles within rooms. He was like "a rabbit running away from a wolf," as the woman described. After ten minutes she finally managed to get him back outside, where the dog immediately returned to his normal self. What was in the corner of that room? Only the dog will ever know.

One thing is certain: every corner of Fort San seems to be haunted, be it by floating light orbs, a sombre nurse or a singing spectre.

NIGHTMARE HOUSE

St. John's, Newfoundland and Labrador

Taking their first steps into their new home on Queen's Road, the young family who purchased the old three-storey row house were excited and happy. But what they hoped would be their dream house quickly became a nightmare.

As soon as they set foot inside, everyone was overcome by an unsettling feeling, a bad vibe. Puzzled, they slowed down and wondered if the others felt something was wrong. No one could tell what was causing the eerie feeling they shared. Everything seemed completely normal about the house. It was old but in decent shape — pleasant, quaint.

As night fell, they began to believe that the bad feeling was just in their heads. They went to bed — and that's when something really strange happened. Faintly they heard a disquieting *scritch-scritch-scritch* sound like nails running down a chalkboard a centimetre at a time. It came from inside the walls. It can be hard enough falling asleep in a new place, but this made it virtually impossible.

Soon after the first night, the family made an unsettling discovery. While brushing off the back step they found it was actually an inscribed tombstone, taken from a cemetery and repurposed for some unknown reason. Every time they stepped out back, it was like they were walking over the dead.

After this macabre revelation, the uneasy feeling of dread in the house worsened. The family felt tense every minute of every day. It seemed like they were being watched in each room. The kids jumped at every opportunity to sleep over at friends' houses, and even the parents found it difficult to get any rest.

Late one night, one of the boys woke to see a dark figure on the other side of his room. Half asleep, he assumed it was his brother. The boy drifted back to sleep as the figure crept toward his bed. When the boy woke in the morning, he found that his clothes had been thrown all about the room. When asked, his brother said he hadn't entered the room or touched the clothing.

That wasn't the last of the nighttime terrors. A little later, three members of the family stood frozen with fear as they watched an orb of red light appear near the staircase. It floated in the air as if it had a mind of its own before suddenly disappearing. Another night, a family friend was grabbed by invisible hands as soon as she passed through the front door. She heard an inhuman moan in her ear, but when she turned around no one was behind her. And shortly after, one of the boys fell asleep on a sofa in the small sitting room on the main floor. When he woke up he couldn't believe his eyes. There, in the middle of the floor, was a wide, dark grave, freshly dug and as wide as a giant mouth. He thought he must be dreaming, but the grave seemed so real he had to jump over it to escape the room. When he finally summoned the courage to show the others, the grave was gone.

This grave incident led the family to seek the council of a Roman Catholic priest. With holy water in hand, the old priest greeted the family and entered the house. He asked the family members to remain downstairs as he investigated the upper floors alone. The family waited, scared but hopeful that the priest would discover what was wrong with the house and cleanse it. They listened to his slow footsteps above. Before long the footsteps sped up as he moved deeper and higher into the house — he wasn't lingering in one place for long. Before completing his investigation of the third floor, the priest hurried back downstairs in a panic. The family asked him what had happened, what he had seen. He couldn't answer. With downcast eyes he shook his head and offered a dire warning: "I would advise you to leave." Without any further explanation, the priest fled from the property, never to return.

They didn't pack up and leave that night, but they didn't last much longer either. Just a few days later, whatever evil presence was haunting their house went absolutely haywire.

Everyone was asleep in their beds. Suddenly, a

tumultuous racket erupted from the main floor. The parents and their children ran downstairs to see what was happening. It sounded like a truck had crashed through the front door and was driving straight through the house, but the truth was much more frightening.

A wooden hatch on the floor that led to a dirty crawl space beneath the house was opening and closing repeatedly: *bang, bang, bang!* The unholy racket was relentless, sending everyone into hysterics. But nothing ever emerged from below. Perhaps that was for the best. As soon as the hatch stopped banging, their bedroom doors flew open and closed upstairs, and something pounded the walls all around them. When the sun finally rose in the morning, it felt like the night had lasted an eternity. But at least the racket had stopped. Shaken and exhausted, the family left. They didn't return.

The family had somehow managed to stay in the hellish house for four months, much longer than most would've lasted. An uncle who didn't believe in ghosts was happy to move in, but he only lived there for a month. He reached his limit when he woke up one morning and looked in the mirror to find angry red scratches running down his spine, all the way from his neck to his lower back.

The house was demolished in 1984 and the lot sat vacant for many years, as if no other building could take root. The land was eventually paved over to create a parking lot. But the family who lived there for four months can't forget what they lived through. One of the boys, now grown up, still suffers from nightmares. In his dreams he's forced back to the site of his childhood trauma. He stands outside the house and looks up. There, in one of the upper-floor windows, is a shadowy form looking back down at him.

The nightmare house — and its poltergeist — lives on in memory.

SENTENCED TO HANG

Victoria, British Columbia

In the mid to late 1800s, Victoria was full of rough-and-tumble men who had travelled to British Columbia seeking their fortunes in the Cariboo Gold Rush. Violence and bloodshed were commonplace. Sir Matthew Begbie presided over fifty-two murder cases, in twenty-seven of which the jury returned a guilty verdict. In those days, hanging was the standard death sentence for murderers, and Begbie soon became known far and wide as the Hanging Judge. Despite his reputation, Sir Begbie was tough but fair, and quite sympathetic toward minorities and the common man.

When the bodies of executed criminals were unclaimed by family, they were unceremoniously buried in unmarked graves. The Provincial Courthouse, now the Maritime Museum, was built directly on top of this mass gravesite, and many people believe this history might explain the amount of paranormal activity that is reported there.

One day in June, Kristy Fallon, a museum employee, was in her office when she was suddenly overcome by an intense sobbing fit. As tears streamed down her face, she began to hyperventilate. She felt nauseated and her knees went weak. A co-worker had to rush her out of the building. It's believed one of the museum's ghosts, a crazed woman who haunts the courtroom, filled Kristy with negative energy. Many years ago the woman sat helplessly, watching her husband being tried and sentenced to death. She is now stuck in the courtroom to grieve for eternity.

Debra Doerksen and Dawn Kirkham, two mediums who have visited the museum on several occasions, have sensed up to forty-five ghosts. They say the museum is full of paranormal energy. When they visited one day with the crew of a local television show, each had a uniquely terrifying experience. Dawn saw a man who had been hanged in the 1880s. Although a length of rope was still tied around his neck, the man appeared confused and unaware that he was dead. He loudly proclaimed his innocence, forever pleading to be set free.

Debra, meanwhile, walked into a cramped and dingy room that was once used as the jail's holding cell and was immediately overcome by a painful tingling sensation in her head. The feeling was caused, she believed, by the spirit energy of a man who long ago repeatedly banged his head against the stone wall in an attempt to avoid his trial. It was an experience that left Debra shaken and in tears.

Sir Matthew Begbie

If you stand outside the Maritime Museum, the site of the old courthouse, and peer in through the front windows, you might catch a glimpse of the Hanging Judge. People have reported seeing a tall, slender man with a long moustache and pointy beard silently gliding down the main staircase. Is he searching for another soul to sentence to hang or upset that his good name has been tarnished after his death? The jury is still out.

UNDER THE KNIFE

Calgary, Alberta

As the sun was beginning to set, a man entered the Riley Park Health Resource Centre, formerly the Grace Hospital. He was there to prepare for his back surgery that had been scheduled early the next morning. He hoped the procedure would bring him some relief, but the night that lay before him would be far from pain-free.

As soon as he stepped into his private room, he froze in his tracks and gasped. There was a woman sitting in the chair by the bed, coolly and silently staring at him. She had long, dark hair and wore a white dress. The man apologized and quickly stepped back into the hall, assuming he must have accidentally walked into the wrong room. But realization slowly washed over him. He hadn't walked into another patient's room. It was the woman in white

who had made the mistake. He stepped back i
the chair was empty. The woman was gone — gc c
time being, that is.

Deeply unsettled, the man turned out the light and
slipped beneath the hospital bedsheet. Maybe, he tried to
convince himself, he had imagined the woman. Maybe the
shadows had played a trick on him, some sort of ghostly
optical illusion. He closed his eyes and, after tossing and
turning, finally fell asleep.

His sleep, troubled as it was, didn't last long. He woke
up when someone walked into his room. *The nurse*, the
man thought, *it must be the nurse checking in on me.*
Muffled footsteps crossed the room. Someone sat on
the bed beside him, the bed squeaking softly under the
weight. And then a hand gently touched his shoulder. The
man rolled over to tell the nurse he was fine, but no one
was there. This happened a few more times throughout
the night, completely disrupting his sleep and fraying his
nerves in the process.

The next morning, a nurse — a real, living nurse —
wheeled his bed into a larger room and told him to hold
tight for a little while. Six or seven other patients were
wheeled into the same room and lined up in a row as the
hospital staff prepared for the day.

"Have you seen my pen?" one of the nurses asked
another. "I just had it."

"Maybe the ghost took it," the second nurse replied.

The row of eavesdropping patients laughed. But the
man scheduled for back surgery remembered the woman
in white sitting in his chair, the sounds of someone

entering his room and sitting on his bed and the cold touch of phantom fingers upon his skin. He didn't join in the laughter.

Neither did the nurse who had suggested that the ghost might have been responsible for the missing pen. "No, seriously," she said without a trace of humour. Her tone was grave. She then told the patients — all of whom had abruptly ceased laughing — that the hospital is haunted. A woman wanders the halls, forever in search of her baby. The woman had died in childbirth and now things go missing all the time.

The man knew then, without a shadow of a doubt, that it was the grieving mother who had scared him so badly the night before. He was too shocked and upset to tell anyone what had happened to him.

The nurses who worked in the Grace Hospital noticed an odd pattern over the years. Time and again, women placed in the same room where the woman had died in labour experienced very difficult deliveries that lasted much longer than most. Many resulted in Caesarean sections, a surgical operation for delivering a child. The nurses came to believe that the ghost was trying to prevent other women from giving birth, perhaps in reaction to what had happened to her. Her ghost has been seen floating solemnly through the halls and has been heard opening windows and rattling the pipes. Occasionally, she gets into a little more trouble.

A guard was stationed in the hospital shortly after the maternity ward closed. That part of the building sat empty and unused before being repurposed, and the guard would often pass some time before the start of his shift in the room where the new mothers used to watch television. He'd been told the story of the ghost who couldn't bring herself to leave the scene of her death, but he chalked that up to the nurses telling tall tales and the other guards trying to spook him. He wasn't a believer, but he soon would be.

One night, the guard arrived to work early as usual. He went to the quiet, empty television room, pulled up a chair and watched an old episode of *Star Trek*. When the time came for him to begin work, he turned off the TV, returned his chair and left the room. As he walked through the halls, he started to feel a little weird. It seemed like someone was watching him, but he was certain he was alone. It was very dark and the red light of the exit signs cast a hellish glow around him.

As he continued on his way, he heard voices coming from a room at the end of the hall. The television room. He approached with caution, stepped inside and saw that someone had turned the TV back on. Someone had also pulled up the chair he had put away earlier. Casting nervous glances around the dark room, he radioed the other guard who was stationed at the desk and asked if anyone else was in the building.

"Just the engineer," the desk guard informed him. But the engineer was in the basement repairing something.

Trying to remain calm and hoping he didn't sound too panicked, the guard explained what had happened.

His colleague laughed. "Must be the ghosts having fun," he said.

Yeah, right, the guard thought. He wanted to laugh

too, but he wasn't in a laughing mood. He turned off the TV, returned the chair for a second time and tried not to look over his shoulder as he left. He could still feel eyes on his back.

As he finished his patrol, the other guard radioed and told him to return to their security base immediately. He sounded anxious and scared. The guard hurried back and asked what the matter was. The desk guard pointed to the security board. A red light was flashing, indicating that someone had pushed a panic button in Operating Room 2, summoning security for help. The guard thought it must be some sort of joke, but his colleague said that no one else had keys to that area of the old maternity ward. Although he didn't want to, the guard had no other option but to go investigate who — or what — had pushed the button.

He slowly entered Operating Room 2, not sure what he'd find. Oddly, it was empty. But there on the wall, the security button was depressed. He pressed it and it popped back out with a click. His colleague radioed to tell him the light on the security board had gone out. The guard left, trying not to give the incident much thought. Better not to dwell on something he had no logical way to explain.

Not halfway back to the security base, his colleague radioed him again. Another light had turned on, this time from Operating Room 1. The guard didn't hesitate. He sprinted to the room and barged inside, determined — perhaps a little frantic — to discover what was going on. Like the previous room, this one was also empty. Once again, the button had been pushed in, ruling out the possibility that a short circuit had triggered the alarms.

Grace Hospital

Not knowing what else to do and feeling at his wits' end, the guard stepped into the hallway. With Operating Room 1 behind him, Operating Room 2 to one side and the television room to the other, he raised his arms and pleaded with whomever might be listening and watching.

"Look," he said. "I know you might feel lonely, as all the babies and mothers are gone now. And I'm sorry that you feel this way. But I have a job to do. My job is to take care of this place and keep it safe. So I'm asking you, please don't keep calling us up here. We need to do our jobs. Thank you, and amen."

For whatever reason, the ghost obliged the guard. As long as he worked there, the security buttons were never pressed again. But that didn't stop the phantom eyes from trailing him as he walked his rounds, forever watching him through the night.

BURIED BELOW

Bonavista, Newfoundland and Labrador

It had been a long, tiring day and the old man wanted nothing more than to return home, crawl into bed and fall asleep. He drove through the night to his house near the Mockbeggar Plantation, a Provincial Historic Site in the small town of Bonavista, and pulled into his driveway. He killed the car's ignition and all was quiet and calm. Wearily, he stepped out of the car and approached his front gate. At the same moment that he opened it, someone opened the door of his enclosed porch.

The old man froze. He couldn't see anyone on the porch or in the yard. The only sounds were the crashing of ocean waves on the nearby shore and the insects buzzing in the grass around the house. He slowly closed the gate. The porch door swung shut as well.

After taking a moment to steel his nerve, the old man crossed the lawn and opened the porch door. The front door to his house followed suit. He closed the porch door behind him and, as before, the front door closed.

The old man opened the front door and stepped inside. Still unable to fathom what was happening, he watched as the kitchen door creaked open slowly.

And then he heard footsteps going up the stairs.

Knowing that his wife would be asleep in their bedroom, and fearful that she was in trouble, the man raced upstairs and barged into their room. He didn't pass anyone on the stairs or in the hall. His wife, alone in the bedroom, sat up in bed with a start. Before she could ask him what was wrong, he demanded to know if she had heard anyone climbing the stairs a moment ago.

"Yes," she said, a slight tremor creeping into her voice. "I thought it was you."

And then, loud at first but slowly fading, they heard the same footsteps walking back down the stairs. This bizarre and unnerving phenomenon occurred on several more occasions.

One day in the spring, the old man was doing some renovations and digging on his property when his shovel hit something solid, something the man never would have expected to discover. Buried deep beneath his house's foundation was a casket. He and his wife had been living for years above a dead body. Once the casket was removed, his doors stopped opening and closing on their own and the couple never heard phantom footsteps going up and down their stairs again.

In any other town, finding a casket buried under your house would be completely unusual, but Bonavista is not any other town. When a canal was dug in the 1920s, the construction crew discovered a number of unmarked coffins buried in the mud. More coffins were unearthed during the construction of a bridge in 1946. The caskets were pried open and the remains of men, women and children were found inside. They were dressed in European-style clothing, and the wood of the coffins was not native to Newfoundland. Experts believe the caskets predate 1725, the year the first cemetery was built in Bonavista.

Where did the coffins come from? Why were they buried in Bonavista? And who were the people left to rot beneath the homes that would later be built above them? Some believe the deceased must have been early French settlers, since many men came from France to fish the Newfoundland coast. Others discredit this theory because French fishermen did not bring their wives or children to Canada. It remains one of the great mysteries of Canada's past, and it's a decidedly macabre mystery to boot.

Whoever they were and however they ended up in their final resting place, the spirits of the departed have not gone quietly into the night. It's not uncommon for people to hear the lilting voices of men and women singing in a foreign language, carried by the midnight wind from the burial grounds where the coffins were discovered.

THE SPIRIT OF THE CATHEDRAL

Quebec City, Quebec

Loud, triumphant music poured from the Cathedral of the Holy Trinity's celebrated organ, filling the building from its pews to its domed ceiling. There was only one man in the church, the organist, and he was concentrating so hard as he practised his music that he didn't hear the sound of approaching footsteps. When he did hear someone approaching, he stopped playing and spun around — the echoes of his music faded to silence. He picked up his sheet music, stood up and peered around the church. Although he could still hear the footsteps getting closer, closer, closer, he couldn't see a soul.

The footsteps grew louder and suddenly stopped to the organist's left. Then the source of the disturbance materialized before his eyes. A woman wearing an old-fashioned dress and hat appeared in front of one of the church's stained-glass windows. Cold sweat trickled into the man's eyes and he could barely breathe. Before he could do anything, the woman disappeared.

A moment later the organ began blaring, an angry sound that reverberated through the air. The organist dropped his sheet music in terror and, as he fled from his instrument and the phantom that was playing it, the blaring turned into a melodic tune not unlike the one the organist had been playing only a minute or two before.

Many have seen the spirit of the cathedral. She has frightened and disturbed organists and churchgoers alike with the sound of her hollow footfalls and tearful moans. Who she is — or rather, *was* — is a bit of a mystery, but it's widely believed that she is one of two women who have deadly ties to the cathedral's early days.

The Cathedral of the Holy Trinity, the first Anglican Cathedral to be built outside the British Isles, was constructed shortly before a cholera epidemic swept through Quebec City. In June of 1832 a few feverish passengers disembarked a ship that had travelled from Ireland to Quebec, and the first known fatality occurred soon after. Within a few short days, cholera had spread to Montreal and into Upper Canada. Suddenly hundreds were dying every day. Doctors were overwhelmed with patients, and officials went to extreme, desperate measures to try to stop the disease from spreading further. Officers fired cannons and the Sanitary Office burned tar in an attempt to cleanse the air.

Iris Dillon lived near the church and in great fear. As scared as she was of the disease that was killing her neighbours and friends, she was even more afraid that she would somehow end up buried alive. Iris suffered from narcolepsy, a neurological disorder that causes people to fall into deep slumbers from which they cannot be roused. Tragically, Iris's greatest fear came true. A neighbour found her in a narcoleptic state and, when he could not wake her, thought she was dead and alerted the authorities. During the epidemic, bodies were dealt with swiftly without prayer or ceremony, and it's believed Iris was buried alive in the church's cemetery. During construction fifty years later, a workman dug up human remains believed to belong to Iris

Organ of the Cathedral of the Holy Trinity

Dillon, who might be the ghost of the cathedral.

The second possibility is a young woman who — approximately thirty years after the cholera epidemic — gave birth to a baby out of wedlock. This was gravely frowned upon in the 1860s, and both the woman and her newborn became social outcasts. Unable to provide for her child and convinced she had no other options, the woman made a horrible decision. Late one night she suffocated her baby with a pillow, crept into the cathedral's basement and buried the small body in the ground beside the remains of entombed bishops. It's rumoured that there's a small, unmarked grave in the cathedral's basement directly beneath the position of the organ.

Some organists have reported that placing toys on the grave has allowed them to practise without the ghostly woman disturbing them. It's believed the young mother, guilt-ridden over her horrific actions, haunts the church seeking forgiveness for the crime she committed more than 150 years ago.

Whether the ghost is a woman who was buried alive or a woman who killed her own child, she's unable to find solace and move on. The cathedral is one of Ghost Tours of Quebec's main stops, and at least two of the leaders have encountered the ghost on separate occasions.

Laurie Thatcher was speaking to a group one night when she saw the ghost standing on the second floor balcony near the organ. Sweat poured down Laurie's face and her heart pounded against her ribcage. She wanted out of the church immediately.

Another night, a different guide had an odd sensation

that she was being watched from behind while she spoke to a group. Shaking the feeling off, she retrieved her lantern — which she had set on a table behind her — and noticed that not only had the light gone out, but the candle had disappeared entirely. Confused and a little shaken, the guide wondered aloud what had happened to the candle. A man on the tour then told her he had seen a shadowy figure standing near the lantern as she spoke.

It seems nothing will bring the spirit any peace, for she still haunts the cathedral today, playing the organ and terrifying people.

ARMY OF THE DEAD

Louisbourg, Nova Scotia

The mid-afternoon sun sparkled across the water of Louisbourg Harbour and warmed the backs of the assembled tourists, giving the tour leader no reason to expect anything sinister lay in wait beyond the chapel door.

Beckoning the group to follow her as she recounted historical tales of what life was like in the Fortress of Louisbourg during the 1700s, the guide opened the door and stepped inside. She had expected the chapel to be empty. It wasn't. A man in period clothing was kneeling at the altar, weeping loudly and shouting in French.

That's odd, thought the guide. There weren't supposed to be any re-enactors, or "animators," in the church. Thanks to restoration efforts by Parks Canada and the Fortress Louisbourg Association, the fortress has been rebuilt by archaeologists and the streets are filled during the summer months with animators, people portraying the rich and the poor, the old and the young, exactly as people lived in 1744. But that church, at that time of day, was supposed to be empty.

The guide did her best to pretend the crying man was a planned part of the tour and carried on spinning tales of the founding of the fortress in 1713 by the French, of its heyday as a thriving fishing settlement and of its eventual destruction in the 1760s at the hands of the British. But the man continued cursing and crying with equal amounts of anger and sorrow, and the guide had to shout to be heard over the racket. Despite her best efforts to remain calm, she lost her train of thought and finally snapped.

She turned to the man at the altar and shouted at him, demanding to know what, exactly, he was supposed to be re-enacting.

The tour guide didn't receive a response. But her group of tourists looked at one another in shock and asked each other why their guide was shouting at an empty altar. The guide was the only person who could see and hear him.

The Fortress of Louisbourg is haunted by an army of the dead, the spirits of soldiers and settlers who lived there long ago. These ghosts, like the man shouting in French in the chapel, are regularly mistaken for the living, breathing animators who recreate history for the visitors of this National Historic Site.

In October, guides lead nighttime tours through the streets of the fortress. It's so large that it includes three authentic eighteenth-century restaurants where stew sim-

mers over open flames, a parlour where women lead dancing demonstrations, the King's Bakery with its delectable
aroma of fresh-baked bread and army barracks where the
ground shakes from the firing of the fortress cannon. It's
so real, Fortress staff say, it seems *surreal*. Surreal is a
very apt choice of word.

On cold autumn nights, the only light comes from the
moon, candles lit in windows and lanterns carried by the
guides. They share some of the more unsettling and mor-
bid stories that have been reported over the years.

At the end of a long, busy night, a guide noticed a candle still burning in one of the barracks's windows. She
entered the building to blow out the candle but was surprised to find a soldier sitting beside the flickering light.
Startled, she breathlessly said, "You'd better hurry up and
get changed. The bus is about to leave." She then blew out
the candle and quickly left. The man didn't answer or follow her out.

After exiting the barracks, she told the bus driver to
wait for the final animator. Everyone on the bus asked
her who she was talking about. "There's still a soldier
up there getting changed," she replied, the first hints of
unease creeping into her voice. "I just spoke to him." The
military supervisor looked at her gravely and informed her
everyone was already on the bus. The last person had left
the barracks ten minutes ago. There was no one — no one
living — inside the barracks.

Sometimes the animators spend the entire weekend
inside the fortress to fully submerge themselves into the
lives of those who lived there during the 1700s. During

Dark study at the Fortress of Louisbourg

one such encampment, an animator who was portraying a member of the French militia was sleeping in the Chevalier house. In the middle of the night she awoke to see three men in British uniform and one First Nations man standing in the large room where others were also sleeping. She assumed the four strangers were fellow animators who had entered the building to find a friend and she rolled over and let herself drift back to sleep. But in the morning, when she described the four men and asked who they were, the British animators shared wide-eyed looks and informed her that they didn't have any uniforms in the style she had seen, nor was there a First Nations man with them. Furthermore, they all insisted that no one in their party had visited the Chevalier house during the night.

Perhaps the creepiest house on the property is the Duhaget home. Captain Duhaget built the house for his wife and the children they hoped to fill it with. Unfortunately, they were unable to conceive a baby, and the captain fell into poor health and died, leaving his wife a widow in the empty home. It's believed the captain couldn't bear the thought of his wife being left alone without children for company, so he took it upon himself to return after death.

When the Duhaget house was being updated for modern-day visitors, the exhibit designer was alone when he saw a uniformed man walk past the stairwell. The stranger's costume was remarkably realistic, particularly his coat. When the exhibit designer later visited the costume department, he told them how impressed he was with the uniforms they had created. Unable to contain her puzzlement, the costume designer informed the man that they did not have any coats in their collection to match his description, and the animators hadn't arrived at the fortress yet. The man could think of only one explanation: he had seen the ghost of Duhaget, and that's why the coat had looked so authentic.

As chilling as the realization that he had seen a ghost was for the poor exhibit designer, perhaps he'd find comfort in the knowledge that Captain Duhaget's ghost seems to be more concerned with protecting guests in his home than terrifying them. One day, when a guide was descending the back stairs, she tripped on the carpet and fell. She would have been seriously injured if not for an invisible hand that reached out of thin air and grabbed her by the shoulder, holding her upright and preventing her from tumbling down to what might have been an early grave.

So real, it's surreal, indeed. Set foot in the Fortress of Louisbourg and you might find yourself marching with the army of the dead.

THE MYSTERY OF BINSTEAD HOUSE

Charlottetown, Prince Edward Island

It was in 1884 that Georgina Mary Pennée found herself in the company of Alfred, Lord Tennyson, the English Poet Laureate. She was visiting her ailing brother who lived in Weston Manor on the Isle of Wight, England, and Lord Tennyson was a neighbour and friend. They sat beside the fire and talked late into the night when Georgina shared a story from her past. A dark, disturbing story, one she hadn't shared widely. It was a ghost story, but it wasn't one she had heard and it most certainly wasn't fictional. It was a story she had lived through while she lived on Prince Edward Island.

Overlooking the Hillsborough River and surrounded by tall, mature trees, the Binstead House sits alone on a large piece of property in Charlottetown, Prince Edward Island. Built in 1833 by John Levitt, Esq., the large home is as white as a ghost and pockmarked by shuttered windows. It was formally recognized as a Historic Place in 1999. It's not common for private residences to receive historic designations for being haunted, but that's how Binstead House rose to infamy.

Georgina was a respectable English woman and the daughter of William Ward, a Director of the Bank of England and one of the era's most celebrated cricket players. Georgina married Arthur Pennée in 1850 and, six years later, they moved into Binstead House.

It was a large home that had chambers for the men hired to farm the estate's fields, making it an abode that was both beautiful and profitable. But the perfect, peaceful facade didn't last long. A mere ten days after the Pennées moved in, strange things started happening.

Late at night, after the last candle had been snuffed and the smell of smoke hung in the air, hair-raising noises wracked the house. It was a rumbling sound that seemed to shake the entire building. Georgina compared it to the noise "produced by dragging a heavy body, which one so often hears in ghost stories." This continued each night for several weeks and was heard in all areas of the house. If only the rumbling was the worst sound the Pennées would hear in their home. Unfortunately, it was not.

As winter turned to spring, the rumbling was accompanied by the shrieks and sobs of an unseen person. The uproar always seemed to start outside, at the base of a tree that stood beside the dining room window. The screams then entered the house and flew from room to room, growing louder and louder, as if some phantom were being chased around the property. Sometimes Georgina heard moaning and muffled words, but the voice was always disembodied. It wasn't until February of 1857 that the source of the phantom voice made itself seen.

Two island women, a Mrs. M. and a Miss C., visited the Pennées as overnight guests. They were set up in a rarely used spare bedroom on the second floor and, after supper and some socializing, retired for the night. The two women slipped into the bed and left the fire burning to keep them warm as they slept. Outside the bedroom window, the gnarled branches of the tree from which the ghostly wails always started reached for the glass pane but fell a little short.

At two o'clock in the morning, Mrs. M. was suddenly awoken by a white light that filled the room. She knew immediately that it couldn't be the fire — it was far too bright. She glanced about the room and saw, standing beside the fireplace, a woman in a checkered shawl with her back to the bed. The light was somehow, inexplicably, flowing straight out of the woman. But Mrs. M. could see that the woman held, in her left arm, a young baby.

Confused and growing a little fearful, Mrs. M. shook Miss C. to awaken her. Suddenly, the woman with the baby spun around and faced them. Her young face was filled with anxiety. Miss C. was convinced their room had been invaded by a ghost. She screamed and pulled the bedsheet over her head and Mrs. M's. They remained covered for the remainder of the night, not daring to peek out from beneath the sheet for fear of what they might see.

The ghost reappeared in the same room the following spring, and this time Georgina witnessed it herself. Her daughter was sick and had moved into the guest room, so Georgina decided to spend the night by her side to keep an eye on her. A little past midnight Georgina got up to fetch some medicine when her daughter noticed a bright light shining under the door from the hall. Believing the light meant her husband was outside, Georgina opened the door quickly and was completely shocked when she found herself face to face with a young woman. The woman held a baby in her left arm and wore a checkered shawl tied across her chest. Georgina knew immediately that this was the same woman her guests had seen before.

The two women — one living, one dead — stared silently at each other, neither able to move or find her voice. Light radiated out of the dead woman and her baby in waves. She looked at Georgina with an agonized stare and then, without so much as a single word, she turned, took a few steps away and disappeared straight through a wall.

After a brief trip home to England, Georgina returned to discover that the creature, as her family and their farm-hands had taken to calling the ghost, had been "carrying on," and that her nightly screams had intensified. A young boy named Harry, who worked on the farm, admitted that the ghost had appeared in his room many times. He refused to share many details of the nighttime visits, but he did reveal that he had often woken from fretful sleeps to see the woman standing at the foot of his bed. Harry refused to allow anyone else to share his room and insisted on locking himself in every night. It was unclear whether Harry hoped to keep the ghost out to protect himself . . . or *in* to protect the others.

The Pennées moved out of Binstead in 1861 and resettled in Quebec. But in 1877 Georgina returned to PEI for several months. One day Father Boudreault, the parish priest, approached her with a letter in his hand, asking if she could shed any light on its contents. It was written by Mrs. Carey, who was the current owner of Binstead. In it Mrs. Carey pleaded with the priest to visit her home to dispel the ghost of a woman with a baby in her arms, a ghost that had troubled her since she'd moved in.

Georgina decided to launch a personal investigation to find the root of the haunting. She discovered that the house was once owned by a farmer named Braddock, who she described as "a man of low tastes and immoral habits." Two sisters, both of whom had baby boys, had worked for Braddock.

Digging a little deeper, a difficult task since respectable people had avoided Braddock due to his character, Georgina learned that one of the sisters had disappeared with one of the babies. But what exactly happened to her was a mystery lost to time. Before the remaining baby turned two, Braddock sold the house and left the area. The remaining sister returned to her parents' house and gave them the baby. It wasn't her baby, she told them, but her sister's. Her own baby, she said sadly, had died. She revealed nothing further and refused to answer their distraught questions, then ran away to America and never returned.

The surviving boy's name was Harry. He was, Georgina realized in shock, the same Harry whom she had hired as a farmhand years later. The same Harry who had been visited by the ghost of a woman holding a baby in her arms. The same Harry who had locked the door and refused to speak on the matter any further.

It's not a stretch to assume that the ghost is Harry's mother, and the baby in her arms his cousin. But puzzling questions remain. How did they die? Did Braddock play a part in their deaths? Why did the sound of the woman's midnight screams always start at the base of the tree? Did the tree have something to do with their deaths, perhaps, or were they buried in the earth at its base?

Georgina found the courage to return to Binstead one final time in 1888. The first thing she noticed was that the ominous tree had been cut down. She then spoke with Mrs. Carey, the woman who had written the letter to the parish priest, and her husband. They revealed that no one had slept in the guest room since they'd occupied the house. Georgina asked if she could spend one night in the room with the ghost, but Mrs. Carey flatly refused. The priest had blessed the house and the matter was closed. Mrs. Carey said no more.

With a little further prodding, Mr. Carey let slip that the ghost had been seen twice since the priest's visit, once near the front entrance and again in an upstairs window. But after a sharp look from his wife, Mr. Carey corrected himself, emphasizing that the ghost had only *allegedly* been seen, as if that somehow made the situation more palatable.

Thus ended Georgina's investigation into the haunting of the Binstead House. Lord Tennyson, riveted by the ghastly tale, requested that Georgina write the story down, and Georgina obliged. A few years later, Georgina's story was discovered by the English Society for Psychical Research, and soon after it became known around the world. It remains one of the most mysterious unsolved ghost cases ever to have occurred in PEI.

SPIRITS OF THE SLIDE

Crowsnest Pass, Alberta

Tours of the Turtle Mountain coal mines, which are nestled in the scenic Municipality of Crowsnest Pass, are offered every fall. Some visitors come for the history, others come for a glimpse into a restricted area and still others come for the claustrophobic thrill of being completely immersed in darkness. It's all in a day's work for the tour guides, but one of them, oddly, has heard the chirping of canaries deep in the bowels of the earth.

Canaries used to be taken into mines to warn the men of carbon monoxide poisoning. If the canaries died, an alarm was sounded and the miners would rush out into the clean air. There are no longer canaries in Turtle Mountain's mines, but the guide is still certain she hears their song calling through the darkness.

It was a separate event that assured her that even when she is alone in the mine, she's never *truly* alone. One night as she prepared for the next tour group, the guide heard the mine shaft door open, followed by voices and the sound of approaching feet. She saw no people, no lanterns, and yet the sound of people came closer and closer. When the sound of the group was practically on top of her, she had a sickening realization. A class of school children was scheduled for the next tour, but the voices in the darkness belonged to grown men. Suddenly the door opened again and the sounds of the men abruptly stopped. She saw lanterns approaching, held in the small hands of children.

When she later told some of the other guides what she had heard, she asked who the first group of men to enter the mine had been. Her companions looked at her like she was crazy. No one else had entered the mine before the children. She had been completely alone.

During the 1800s, the First Nations people of southern Alberta avoided Turtle Mountain. They called it the "mountain that moves," and one of their legends claimed a tragedy would occur there. Little did the citizens of the community of Frank know that the mountain that towered more than 2,100 metres above them would indeed move. And it would completely eradicate nearly everything that stood in its path.

At 4:10 a.m. on April 29, 1903, 82 million tonnes of limestone broke free from the mountain and roared down its slope into Crowsnest Pass. The limestone broke apart into colossal boulders that destroyed 75 percent of Frank, buried the entrance to the mine, ploughed across the valley and even climbed approximately 150 metres up a neighbouring mountain. Of the town's six hundred inhabitants, more than seventy people lost their lives. It was,

Debris field from the landslide that destroyed Frank, Alberta

and still is to this day, Canada's biggest and deadliest rock slide.

Today, the rocks remain where they fell, forming a giant graveyard above the land where many of the bodies could not be retrieved from the rubble. Monica Field, who works for the Frank Slide Interpretive Centre, is aware of the ghost stories that have sprouted from the area's history. She calls it, "an area of such concentrated suffering." How could it not be home to a spectre or two?

Children who live nearby make sport of climbing the massive boulders left behind by the slide. But no one, if they're being honest, ever feels quite right in the area. They report an uneasy, sickening feeling of being watched at all times. Hikers have crested hills only to see the silhouettes of miners staring down on them from farther up the mountain. And it's said that an archaeologist was accosted by the ghost of a miner wielding a pickaxe, warning the archaeologist to leave. He did, and quickly.

The eerie feeling that permeates the air might be caused by the fact that so many lives were lost in such a short period of time. The rock slide was a tragedy that was over in a minute and a half, but it appears as if some of its victims now remain tied to this world for an eternity.

SPOOKY HOLLOW

Norfolk County, Ontario

Picture yourself driving through Normandale, a small, sleepy town not unlike the countless others that dot Canada's vast countryside. Your car drives up a steep hill, past harvested fields and the Gothic-style gates of a small cemetery. At the top of the hill you see a sign and must make a choice: turn right and continue on your way, or continue straight ahead toward Spooky Hollow.

Ghostly legends and lore abound in Spooky Hollow, which isn't surprising given its creepy name, which could have come straight out of a fairy tale — one of the dark, scary ones where things don't necessarily end happily ever after.

Once long ago, during an unusually warm day in early fall, a young Normandale couple named Peter and Janet spent a relaxing day at the beach not too far from their hometown. As the sun began to dip behind the silhouetted pine trees on the horizon, they packed Peter's car and started for home. Night fell upon them as they drove along the twisty country roads, the car's headlights reflecting off animal eyes in the woods. It was a humid night and they drove with the windows down, enjoying the wind and fresh air. Long, wispy tendrils of fog crept out from between the trees, but Peter didn't let that bother him. Not wanting the day to end, he decided he'd take the scenic route home. He turned off the paved highway, onto the gravel road that snaked through the heart of Spooky Hollow.

The fog thickened as the forest became denser, darker. It was hard to see more than a few feet in front of the car, and Peter had to slow to a crawl. Suddenly, the car's engine backfired and the vehicle jumped. The couple cried out in shock. Peter pushed down on the gas pedal, but instead of accelerating, the car slowly came to a stop. Peter tried to restart it, but nothing happened. The engine was dead. They looked under the hood but had no idea how to fix the car. So Peter volunteered to walk to the nearest farmhouse — there had to be one nearby, although he couldn't remember passing one in a long, long time — and ask to use their phone to call a tow truck. He told Janet to stay in the car, lock the doors and stay warm under a blanket. He'd return soon.

He didn't. An hour passed, then two, then three, but still there was no sign of him. Janet grew increasingly scared and concerned. He should have been back long ago. Eventually Janet grew so tired that even her fear couldn't keep her awake, and she slipped into a troubled sleep.

She didn't sleep for long. A loud thump rocked the hood of the car and startled her awake. Her heart jumped into her throat and she peered out into the dark fog but could see nothing.

"Peter?" she called out uncertainly, hoping her boy-friend had returned.

A second bang shook the car, the only response to her call. She yelled and pulled the blanket up to her chin, fro-zen with fear. Fortunately, Peter soon returned with help, but when Janet told him what had happened and he inves-tigated the area, he found no trace or sign that anyone had been near the car. The only explanation the couple could fathom was that the car had been struck twice by one of the ghosts that gave Spooky Hollow its name.

Some say a travelling salesman once sought refuge in a stranger's home where he met a grisly end. A wicked storm made it impossible for his horse to carry on any further and he knocked on the door of the first house he came upon. Luckily, he thought, the owner welcomed him in. But he turned out to be anything but lucky. He was murdered and dismembered in the middle of the night, and the sky above was choked for days with black smoke that spewed from the house's chimney. Those who passed by noticed that a pungent, repulsive smell accompanied the smoke, giving rise to the belief that the salesman's body was burned in the fireplace to destroy evidence of the murder.

Others believe a gang of criminals who illegally trans-ported alcohol from Canada to the United States in the

1920s, during Prohibition, haunt the woods. One day they were ambushed and gunned down by the local law enforcement, soaking the dirt with their blood and trapping their spirits in the forest.

But the story that has gained the most notoriety involves a small hotel that once sheltered travellers more than one hundred years ago. The hotel caught fire one night and was reduced to cinders and ash. Not everyone was able to escape. Someone died in the blaze. And as you might imagine, the victim's ghost is none too fond of fire.

Only the bravest human beings can tell you if this is true, but if you want to experience the scare of a lifetime you should venture into Spooky Hollow on Halloween. Find a secluded clearing in the woods — anywhere will do. Wait for night to fall. When the clock strikes midnight, light a match and listen closely. As the flame burns down you'll hear agonizing screams in the distance, as pain-ridden and real as the day the victim died in the fire.

PHOTO CREDITS

HAUNTED CANADA

Read the whole chilling series.

978-0-7791-1410-8

978-0-439-96122-6

978-0-439-93777-1

978-1-4431-2893-3

978-1-4431-3929-8

978-0-545-99314-2

978-1-4431-2894-0

For Haunted Canada bonus material,
visit www.scholastic.ca/hauntedcanada.